First Edition — 2001

Library of Congress Control Number: 2001131757

ISBN: 1-931600-00-7

Printed in the United States of America

Through Her Hymns and Those Who Sing Them!

The Most Complete History Ever Written

Edited by Jack Clark

This book is dedicated to our precious little grandson, Collin.

Foreword

I have had a long-time fascination with, and a deep admiration for,the creative lyrical abilities of Fanny Crosby and for her obvious dedication to the cause of Christ. It is then no wonder that I was overjoyed to become friends a few years ago with Dennis and Darlene Neptune.

Darlene Neptune is, without doubt, the world's leading authority on the life and works of Fanny Crosby. She has traveled to Fanny's birthplace, she has visited the place where Fanny went to school, she has toured Fanny's home and she has visited Fanny's final resting place. She has researched and documented many of the thousands of hymn texts Fanny wrote, even to determining the fact that Fanny did, indeed, write many hymns under a variety of assumed names. Darlene speaks of Fanny's husband, of her child, of the heartbreak of losing that child and of her will to go on with her work after the tragedy.

We learn also, from Darlene, about the political activism of Fanny Crosby, about the fact that she was personal friend and spiritual adviser to every president who held office during her lifetime, about her love for children and of her provision of a place where unfortunate young ladies could seek haven.

I have been fortunate, on numerous occasions, just to sit and listen to Darlene tell of her search for facts and figures and I have been witness to her costuming herself and presenting her monologue of Fanny's life. I was spellbound!

Prepare yourself for an interesting journey through the life and times of a remarkable lady. It was Fanny's ambition to reach a million people with the gospel of Jesus Christ....an ambition that has no doubt been fulfilled many times over.

Jack Clark
Cleveland, Tennessee

Contents

A Chance Encounter

I lost my balance! The tombstone upon which I was leaning disappeared! Things looked different, even the clothes I was wearing changed! The trees in the cemetery appeared smaller and there were a lot less graves off in the distance.

Could it be? Had I gone back in time? Fear gripped me. Then a calm came over me as I thought…I told God I would like to go back in time. Now I was shocked; He had given me what I asked for. I stood up and I looked around. Could it really be? Was I in…. what year was it?

Moments before I was sitting upon the grave of Frances Jane Crosby, better known as Fanny Crosby, the great hymn writer. I shared with the Lord that I would have loved to have met this wonderful Saint of God. O Lord, I thought if I could just go back in time. Then it happened!

I stood still for a moment trying to gain my composure. Okay, I asked for it. Now what will I do?

There was an elderly man visiting a grave not far away. Surely he knew what year it was. "excuse me sir; I seem to have lost my way." As he looked up I saw tears in his eyes.

"Oh, I'm sorry if I have bothered you."

"Nonsense," he said in his broken English. "I always get this way when I visit the grave of my dear wife. We spent many years together. She lived a long life, I miss her so."

I see on the gravestone that she died in 1910.

"Seventy years she lived and fifty of those with me. For four years I have visited her on Sunday afternoon."

Four years…that meant it was 1914!!!

"Are you here to visit someone?"

"Not really. I have just arrived in Bridgeport on business and decided to take a walk."

"The park is at the beach! It is a good walk but not too far, that way," he said as he pointed a way out of the cemetery. "There are always a lot of people in the park on Sunday afternoons."

We visited a while and I went my way. As I left the cemetery I passed people living their lives as though nothing unusual had happened. They were, of course, in 1914! No one seemed to notice I had just appeared, or should I say backed into this century.

It was a lovely Sunday afternoon and the one thing that struck me was the calm. People were walking, visiting on porches, there was laughing, children playing. On the streets were horse-drawn carriages, an occasional lone rider, bicycles and bicycles built for two.

My curiosity was getting the best of me. I was actually beginning to enjoy myself! Businesses were closed. There didn't seem to be a care in the world. Everyone was so relaxed! Finally I came to the park, a beautiful view of the beach. Just as he said, it was full of people. Women in 1914 apparel, some carrying parasols to block the sun from their lily white skin. The courting couples were obvious; they were holding hands and the gentlemen carried the parasols. What a serene time.

Making my way through the park I was approached by a woman.

"Excuse me," she said, "I heard you humming the song *Blessed Assurance.*"

I didn't realize that I was.

"Do you know Aunt Fanny?" she said.

"No, I do not, but I do love her music. Is she your Aunt?"

"No, she is a dear friend of mine. Would you like to meet her?"

"Oh yes, I would." She led me across the park to a small gathering of picnicking people.

On the blanket sat a tiny figure in dark glasses.

"Aunt Fanny, I met this lady walking in the park humming one of your hymns."

A smile came across the face of that tiny creature.

"Which song was it"? Fanny asked.

"Blessed Assurance."

"Oh, I do hope it is a blessing to you."

I could not believe my eyes or my ears. I was looking at and talking to Fanny Crosby! Could this possibly be real?

"It is a blessing to me, one of my favorite hymns." I longed to tell her that nearly one hundred years from today it would still be the favorite of many!

"We must be going." she said.

"It has been such an honor to meet you Miss Crosby, I have always loved your music."

"What is your name, dear?"

"Darlene, Darlene Neptune!"

"That is a different name, Greek?"

"Yes, ma'am, it is."

"It has been nice to meet you, you must stop and visit sometime."

"Stop by?"

"Yes, my place. You do know that I no longer live on State Street. Carrie and I moved in with our niece, Florance, at 226 Wells Street in 1906. You are most welcome to stop by there anytime. Please do."

A tall, thin, middle-aged gentleman placed her hand around his arm and off they went; Fanny, the gentleman and several ladies who accompanied them.

I stood there in shock. Could it be? I just met Fanny Crosby! I continued my walk and felt as though I were floating on air.

As the day wore on I decided to attend church that evening. I found a vast choice of places to worship. Remembering that Fanny was a member of the Methodist Episcopalian Church in downtown Bridgeport, there was no doubt that's where I would attend. After the service a woman asked if I was new in town. "I am here to do some research," I answered.

"My name is Eva," she said, and proceeded to ask where I would be staying and where were my things?

Well, that was something in all my excitement I had forgotten about. "I have not found a place to stay and I seem to have lost my suitcase." This was not a lie...my clothes where somewhere in Bridgeport, only where? She offered me a room in her home and I graciously accepted. I continued: "I am in town to write a story about Fanny Crosby and praying that the Lord will give me the information I need." After sharing about the chance meeting in the park Eva proceeded to explain that the Lord was truly leading, more than I knew. Her full name was Eva Cleaveland. She was Fanny Crosby's personal secretary!

That evening as I retired I thought about my day. What a day!

As a child I was curious, rambunctious and a bit mischievous. As far back as I can remember my imagination was always reaching out somewhere, my mind never seemed to be still. Always busy!

During church services I was restless, thumbing through the index of Composers and Authors in the hymnal and it took no time to realize that Fanny Crosby had written many of the hymns. There was something different about the way she wrote. The words seemed to flow divinely from God. The message was always easy to understand, even for a child.

One year, for my birthday, I was given a book about her life. Immediately something clicked as I read. We were different, yet alike. We were both born with a strong curiosity about the world, although our worlds were different times and places. I would see the world with eyes. God would speak to me through sight and thought. Because of her blindness Fanny would see the world through touch. God would speak to her through touch and thought.

We were both born with a keen sense of mischief. We were both born with the ability to laugh at ourselves and neither of us had trouble expressing ourselves on any occasion. We were both born with the inability to sit still. We had to be doing something constantly and it would be through this energy that God would eventually do His work.

I could not absorb enough information about this lady. I had to know more.

Each year my concert and women's ministry tours took us to the New England shores where I visited libraries to find more information. I began to be suspicious that Fanny wrote many hymns under different names? I was determined to know all I could.

Now Here I was, in Bridgeport, Connecticut, in 1914!!!

Second Meeting

I awoke to a whole new day. What would I do first? Every ounce of me hit the floor running the minute my eyes were open.

Eva gave me some clothing and, at breakfast, announced she was taking me to meet Fanny for a personal interview. She told how Fanny would sit on her porch daily welcoming friends and strangers who came to visit. These people were important to Fanny and I would have to work around them.

"Do they come all year round?"

"Yes."

"In the winter?"

Eva explained, "Fanny hates winter but visitors never let the cold stop them from coming."

After breakfast we left the house of Eva Cleaveland. Riding on the brick streets I closed my eyes and listened to the sound of the horses hoofs and wagon wheels. It was a strange sound to my ears. I remembered reading how Fanny talked of hearing the sound of horses hoofs, how she knew when they came to a cross street.

That sound was different caused by the crosswise running of the bricks and ruts. I thought how acute her hearing must be!

We arrived at 226 Wells Street. Sitting in her rocking chair on the front porch was Fanny Crosby, visiting with several neighborhood children and reading a book she had put together. The book consisted of four pages of color; black for sin, red for Christ's blood, white for right and gold for Glory. I listened as she told her story and shared the pages of the book. I found myself on the porch leaning against the banister, huddled among the children. I was in awe. I was also, once again, struck by how tiny a person she was. About four feet nine, small in frame, her white hair pulled up into a bun. Her hands were tiny and she wore a ring on both ring fingers. I guessed she could not weigh one hundred pounds if wet! The year was 1914 but her dress looked more 1870ish. Her tiny feet were clad in high top boots. She was neat and clean in appearance.

When the children left, Eva and I were invited inside for tea. I sat quietly, listening to the chatter, in awe of it all. It was interesting just watching, looking at the clothing of the day. Fanny dressed in a past era style, puffy sleeves to the elbow then lace continuing down to the mid-hand, skirt floor length and full at the bottom. She was in summer dress, beige in color, boots were beige and covering the ankle. Florance and Eva were more in style with the time, reflecting their ages. Theirs were high neck blouses, lots of lace on fronts, wide at the shoulders and slimming to reveal tiny waists. Slim fitting skirts with a small flounce at the bottom, both were light in color. Florance was a bit heavier than Eva but not by much. Henry wore a neatly starched white shirt, open at the neck with suspenders holding neatly pressed beige color linen breeches. All were very neat in appearance.

After tea Fanny and Eva took care of some business, writing return letters while I visited with Florance, or Flo as Fanny called her, and Florance's husband Henry. It was Florance and Henry Booth's home in which Fanny was now living. Fanny and her sister Carrie came to live with Flo and Henry in1906 when Carrie was diagnosed with intestinal cancer. Florance was the daughter of William, son of Fanny's step-father, Thomas Morris. She was not direct blood but Fanny knew her since birth and felt a deep love for her. Flo and Henry both loved Fanny dearly and wanted to supply her with all the comforts during her final years.

Finally the time came when Fanny was all mine.

"Good morning Darlene. Beautiful summer morning."

"It is so wonderful to have met you Miss Crosby and to have this time to spend with you." I was so glad that Fanny could not see me; I could not stop staring into her face. I was really talking with Fanny Crosby!

"I know that I am not your Aunt, but you may call me Aunt Fanny, all of my friends do."

"I see you are holding a little book, not the same one as earlier?"

"Yes, as a child I never knew what to do with my hands. Mother gave me this little book to carry. I have carried it with me for many years. As I grew older it seemed as I caressed it the words would flow more freely. I would hold it close during late night hours when I composed my hymns."

"I have so many questions I'm not sure where to begin."

"Well, what is your most pressing question?" Fanny asked.

"May I ask you anything?"

"You may."

"When did you first realize that you would always be blind?"

Fanny began her story...

Permanent Blindness

"My mother, Mercy, would for many years feel guilty about my blindness. She would refuse to accept it as a fact. When I was just 5 years old, mother took me by boat to Sing Sing (now Ossining), near New York City, to visit a Dr. Valentine Mott, a renowned eye specialist. This would be my first taste of New York and city life—it would remain with me forever.

"Mother became ill on the sloop so I was left to the care of the Captain. I would entertain him by singing a few songs as we sailed down the Hudson. The captain of the ship would later describe me by saying, 'She was a fairly pretty child with black hair and a frisky disposition.'

"When we arrived in the city mother and I stayed with a friend for a few days. I was perplexed at the noise, it was indeed a great contrast to the quietness of our rural home.

"Our meeting with Dr. Mott was both exciting and frightening. I knew that mother wanted me to have the use of my eyes. Dr. Mott gave me some toys to play with and that seemed to be my fondest memory of the entire trip.

"Dr. Mott asked if I would like him to do something for my eyes that would make me see? No sir, I replied promptly, moving nearer to my mother for I was afraid that might mean he would need to hurt me. The kind physician put his hand on my head and said, 'Poor child, I am afraid you will never see again.'

"I could feel my mother's disappointment, but I could not understand why she should be so anxious concerning me. As we sailed home I sat there on the deck amid the glories of departing day, the low murmur of the waves soothed my soul into a delightful peace.

"I would later compose this poem:

Oh, what a happy soul I am,
Although I cannot see,
I am resolved that in this world
Contented I will be.

How many blessings I enjoy
That other people don't!
To weep and sigh because I'm blind
I cannot nor I won't."

"It is amazing to me that you weren't angry about being blind."

"I did not have the time nor did I ever consider being angry. I knew that there were things I wanted to do. My main concern was that no teachers knew how to teach a blind child. I wanted so much to be like the other children."

"But you did receive an education.... didn't you?"

"Oh yes, an excellent one."

"How?"

Finding A School / Leaving Home

"Oh, thank God, He has answered my prayer, just like I knew He would. I said clapping my hands in excitement. That day was the happiest day of my life, for the dark intellectual maze which I was living in seemed to yield to hope and the promise of the light that was about to dawn. I did not crave physical vision for it was mental enlightenment that I sought and now my quest seemed almost actually rewarded.

"It was November of 1834, when mother called me to her side. 'The postman has just delivered a letter,' she said, 'sent by a friend.' It was a circular from a school in New York City called the New York Institution for the Blind.

"The New York Institution was a foreign name to me but it was enough to know that some place existed where I might be taught; and my star of promise even then was becoming a great orb of light.

"Mother could obviously see and feel my excitement but to test me she asked, 'What will you do without me? You have never been away from me for more than two weeks at one time.'

"Much as I love you, mother, I am willing to make any sacrifice to receive an education.

Mother said that I was right and she was glad I had the chance to go but her voice betrayed the tremor in her heart. How wonderful a mother's love, I thought. One month later, on March 3rd, 1835, when I was fourteen, I went to New York. Mother awakened me from a sound sleep and told me the stage was at the front door. The thought of going away thoroughly unnerved me; I dressed with trembling fingers, hastily ate a few mouthfuls of breakfast, swallowed my sobs and then quickly hurried from the house lest I might break down completely if I waited to bid mother goodbye. You can imagine my feelings as the stage rumbled on and on toward Norwalk, Connecticut where we were to take the steamboat for New York. My suffering was indeed intense. For more than an hour I said nothing. The lady who accompanied me tried to cheer me.

"She said if I didn't want to go to New York we could take the returning stage home. I hesitated and broke into tears; and after a good cry I said, no, I will go to New York. That decision I never for a moment regretted for had I returned to my mother that morning I would have cast away my pearl of great price. It is not probable that I should ever have been brave enough to start again for the Institution.

"From Norwalk we went and later that day we gently sailed into the harbor of New York. On Saturday, the morning of March 7, 1835, my escort and I were driven to the New York Institution for the Blind on Ninth Avenue. Everyone treated me with great love but I missed my childhood friends and most of all my mother. In the evening I was taken to a room that was to be mine. Everything was strange, nothing was in its proper place — I could not stop thinking about home.

"I bravely tried to think of only pleasant things. It was no use, however, for I could not keep the curl from coming to my upper lip; I sat there on my trunk, a forlorn being indeed, and sighed heavily. Our matron, a motherly Quaker woman, put her arms about me and said, 'Fanny, I guess thee has never been away from home before.' I replied meekly, no ma'am, and please excuse me, I must cry. I burst forth into the flood of tears that I had tried so hard to restrain. When the fit of weeping passed, one of my fellow pupils came and sat down with me on the trunk; and for a whole hour we talked about everything but home. By the next morning the worst of my homesickness had passed."

"You have really piqued my curiosity, Aunt Fanny. The more you tell me, the more questions I have. I am afraid that I will wear you out with all of my questions...or maybe forget to ask one."

"Let me give you a copy of my autobiography, **Memories of Eighty Years.** You may take it with you. Any questions I do not answer or questions you think of later, the answers may be in here. Also, Eva keeps a diary about my days. Do check with her on some things. Now, why don't we just start at the beginning?"

"Sounds good to me! Where were you born?"

Fanny As A Small Child

"I was born into a rural setting, a place of wonderful wilderness and grandeur. These gracious gifts of natural scenery left their own indelible imprint upon my mind for, although I was deprived of sight at the age of six weeks, my imagination was still receptive to all the influences around me. The surrounding country with its own native beauty was real enough to me; in one sense as real to my mind as to the minds of my little companions.

"Near the humble cottage where we lived ran a tiny brook, a branch of the Croton River. The rippling of the water was music to my ears. I would sit on a large rock near the stream. The voices of nature enchanted me, they all spoke a familiar note. Sometimes in the song of a bird or the buzz of a bee, the locust in the shade or the piping cricket at night, I felt the fairies themselves were bringing messages directly to me.

"I was born in Southeast, New York (Southeast is the name of the town), near Brewster, New York, in Putnam County. We had a small house, a duplex in which mother, father and I lived on one side and grandmother, grandfather and their children lived on the other.

"When I was six weeks of age a slight cold caused an infection in my eyes which appeared to demand the attention of the family physician. He not being at home, a stranger was called, who recommended the use of hot poultices which ultimately destroyed the sense of sight. When this sad misfortune became known throughout our neighborhood, the unfortunate man thought it best to leave. We never heard of him again. But I have not for a moment, in more than ninety-four years, felt a spark of resentment against him because I have always believed from my youth to this moment that the good Lord, in His Infinite mercy, by this means consecrated me to the work that I am still permitted to do.

"At the age of 10 months my father, John, died of pneumonia leaving mother to raise me with only the help of my grandmother, Eunice."

"Can you tell me more about your mother? What was her life like, raising a blind child? It must have been hard as a widowed mother."

Birthplace of Fanny Crosby as it looked in 1820
Southeast, New York

Mercy Crosby

Mercy Crosby Morris

Throughout her life Fanny remained close to her mother. Her mother worked hard to support herself and Fanny after the death of her husband, John.

On Mercy's eighty-second birthday Fanny presented her with this poem which she had written:

How pleasant to look on a brow like hers,
with hardly a trace of care;
How cheerful the light of her beaming eye,
as she sits in her easy chair.

So little the change in her dear, kind face
We scarce can believe it true
That she numbers today her four score years,
Her four score years and two.

Her winter of age, though the snowflakes fell,
Has never been dark and drear,
She moves with the vigor of younger feet,
And her mind is bright and clear.

She merrily talks of the olden time,
Of the friends in youth she knew;
She is sprightly and gay, though she numbers today
Her four score years and two.

And now as we come with our birthday gifts,
When she views them o'er and o'er,
And the earnest God bless you, my children dear,
Is breathed from her lips once more.

We think how devoted our mother's love,
What a sunshine of joy she gives,
And we feel as we tenderly kiss her cheek,
What a comfort that still she lives!

"My dear mother, who was so many years a comfort to me, passed peacefully from this world to that brighter home above, September 2, 1890. She lived to attain the grand old age of ninety-one years and always enjoyed good health until a short time before her death. Her last days were calm and beautiful, a blessing to all who knew her. As a tribute of my devotion to her, I composed the following poem:"

Mother

Her voyage of life is ended,
Her anchor firmly cast,
Her bark that many a storm has, braved
Is safe in port at last.

Surrounded by her treasured ones,
Our mother passed away
Beneath the golden sunset,
Of summer's brightest day.

"She waited for the summons,
That called her to depart,
And heard the voice of Jesus,
Like music in her heart.

Not hopeless in our sorrow,
We lay her down to sleep,
Where He, our Lord and Saviour,
A hallowed watch will keep.

"We loved our tender mother,
Far more than words can tell,
And while with deep emotion,
We breathe our fond farewell.

We know her tranquil spirit,
Has reached the longed-for shore,
And now with joy is greeting,
The loved ones gone before.

"Oh, mother, we are coming;
The time will not be long
Till we shall clasp thy hand again,
And join the blessed song.

The sheaf of wheat is garnered,
The sickle's work is done,
And everlasting glory,
Through Christ her soul has won.

"What was your relationship with your grandmother like?"

"I was close to my grandmother. I credit her for many things in my life. She taught me about animals, flowers, trees, people and whole books of the Bible. She was my brightest window to the world."

An Extraordinary Woman
Eunice Crosby – Fanny's Grandmother

Somewhere, sometime, behind every great man or woman of God there is an important someone, the somebody nobody knows about. Eunice was Fanny's somebody! She was an extraordinary woman. When Mercy was depressed with Fanny's blindness Eunice would quote these lines from the old hymn:

Though troubles assail and dangers affright,
Though friend should all fail and foes all unite;
Yet one thing assures us, whatever betide,
The scripture assures us the Lord will provide.

"Not only did my grandmother have the task of keeping mother's spirits up but she decided early I would not be helpless. She taught me all that she knew of the world and tried to stretch my imagination further than anyone could have thought possible.

"She taught me to believe in God and to ask Him for any need. Grandmother was always kind but firm. She was determined that I would learn and would not be spoiled.

"She was not well educated yet was aware of how to teach me by making me feel things; a thorny bush, a bird, different flowers, the count of their petals, their shape and their smell.

From grandmother I learned how many horses were around by the sound of their hoofs. The difference between the smells of a horse, a pig, a chicken and the rest of God's creatures. I would not just learn by smell but the feel of their shapes. Grandmother was quick to realize how bright a child God had given her to teach.

"From an early age my memory was remarkable. I was shown or heard something one time and would forever remember it."

"Fanny, I pause to think how wonderful God is for He placed you in that family. In all of His wisdom He knew Eunice would not give up on you. God knew she would shape you into the tool that He would someday use. What an awesome responsibility and yet, instead of feeling sorry for you, she was busy about God's work."

"At evening time grandmother would call me to her rocking chair where we would kneel down and repeat some simple petitions. I later wrote a poem about this:

There are forms that flit before me,
There are tones I yet recall,
But the voice of gentle grandma
I remember best of all.

In her loving arms she held me,
and beneath her patient care
I was borne away to dreamland
In her dear old rocking chair.

"Once Grandmother caught a butterfly and made me touch it. It's wings were little more than stiff fuzzy paper. It didn't buzz or vibrate like a fly, it flittered and I could feel its wings beat. I remember raising my hand and feeling the butterfly lift away flying free.

"Another time she slapped my hands for some breach of good behavior. This grieved me greatly and at once bitter resentment sprang up in my heart. Thinking to soothe me, a little companion called me out to play with him. As I went, something within said, Yes, I will play with you, but I will hurt you for grandma has hurt me. I threw a stone at him but missed my aim. The cloud soon passed and all was sunny again. Fifty years later, to my surprise, when I was lecturing in Yonkers, New York, a man whispered in my ear. 'Do you remember David Ketcham, your early playmate?' Certainly, I remembered him and we had a good laugh over the incident."

"It sounds to me as if your family was religious. Where did they attend?"

"We attended the Old Southeast Church. It was Presbyterian."

"Did you live in Southeast on Fogginton Road until you left for the New York Institution for the Blind?"

Life Among the Quakers

A"t the age of three mother and I moved to North Salem in neighboring Westchester County. I missed grandmother so much that mother gave me a pet lamb. Through the fields and meadows we would romp. Occasionally I would fall asleep under some old tree and would wake to find my pet beside me. But soon, he grew into a strange animal that would knock me down, tear my dress and make me cry. For a time I would forgive him and then one day he disappeared. Not many days after that we had mutton for dinner. My pet had not returned and I knew at once what had happened to him. I refused to eat meat that day and slipped off into a corner so as not to betray the tears that I could not restrain. Another farmer offered to give me a lamb but I refused. I reasoned, why should I again be deprived of a dear pet? I will have none and then there will be no chance of it."

"Did you have any spiritual training there?"

"While living in North Salem, mother and I would attend the Quaker Meeting House near Peach Pond. We remained there for five years among the Quaker families."From there mother and I moved to Ridgefield, Connecticut. There I would receive a deep spiritual training."

"How long were you in Ridgefield and what did your mother do there?"

Spiritual Training

When I was eight, mother and I moved to Ridgefield, Connecticut. Mother took a job as housekeeper for one of the wealthy Quaker families. Their name was Hawley. Mr. Hawley owned and operated a successful buggy company in Ridgefield. Having no children of her own at home, Mrs. Hawley, a kind Christian lady, decided to tutor me. Through Mrs. Hawley, I acquired much knowledge of the Bible. She would assign me a number of chapters each week and by the end of the first year I knew the first four books of the Old Testament and the four Gospels. That year in Sunday school I was presented with a Bible for reciting more verses than any other. I remember Mrs. Hawley with gratitude and affection. One afternoon Mrs. Hawley said to me: 'Fanny, I believe that God has permitted your blindness in order to serve His purposes.'

"I learned one very important lesson. Mrs. Hawley had several hundred rose bushes in her front garden and I could pick any of them except from her prized white roses. One day a friend of mine was over and he wanted one of those white roses. I told him no but he insisted, so I gave him one. What I did not know was that Mrs. Hawley was watching out her window. Later that day Mrs. Hawley called me to her side and said, 'Fanny do you know who picked the white rose from the bush yonder?' I told her no, thinking she would put it behind her. Later that evening Mrs. Hawley read me the story of Ananias and Sapphira. I'll tell you, from that moment on, I told no more falsehoods to my good friend."

"Did you see your grandmother much while living in Ridgefield?"

"I would continue to frequently journey back to the town of Southeast to visit with her, she remained to live there in the house where I was born.

"My family members were Calvinist Presbyterians and I remember hearing the choir singing some of the beautiful hymns. It was the custom for one of the deacons to compose a hymn to be sung to some standard tune. These homely productions possessed some genuine merit. One of them I can remember contained the following stanzas:

Kind Father, condescend to bless
Thy sacred word to me,
That, aided by Thy heavenly grace,
I may remember Thee.

And when life's journey shall be o'er,
Thy glory may we see;
Dear Savior, I will ask no more
Than this, Remember me.

"It was the music of the Methodists that attracted me. In 1851 I became a member of the Methodist Church and have remained so the rest of my life.

"During my time in Ridgefield my desire for knowledge was increasing, but I found that the teacher in the village school, to which I often went with the children of my own age, was too busy to give me the personal help which I needed.

"One evening while alone in my room, I knelt down near the window and asked the Lord to show me how I could learn like other children.

"At that moment the weight of anxiety that burdened my heart changed to the sweet consciousness that my prayer would be answered in due time. If I had been restless and impatient before, from that time forth I was still eager, but confident that God would point the way for me to gain the education I craved. As I already said, I felt no resentment against the poor physician who destroyed my eyes but I was not content to live in ignorance; and, in the course of time, in a way of which I had no previous intimation, my wish was to be granted in the fullest measure."

"Your strong desire to learn is amazing to me. When most children would be busy at play you were worrying about how to receive an education. Most children try to find an excuse not to go to school and you prayed to go."

"I truly believe the good Lord had His hands on me from the minute I was born. He led me to one of the finest schools. It was famous around the world as a premier place for teaching the blind. Let me share with you some information that I have on the school. Eva, Eva."

Eva joined us on the porch, "Yes, Aunt Fanny what can I do for you?"

"Eva, would you try to find the information on the blind school?"

Within minutes Eva handed me a package about the Institution.

The Institution for the Blind, New York

The New York Institution for the Blind

When I entered the school in 1835, I was the thirty-first pupil. By the end of 10 years there were over 100 students. New York City had grown wonderfully in many ways since 1835 and the advance in knowledge and education was no less rapid than its material prosperity. I well remember the time when Kipp and Brown's stages were the sole means of rapid transit in the city and they only went up as far as Twenty-sixth Street unless by special order. Our buildings were situated on Thirty-fourth Street and Ninth Avenue in the midst of a delightful suburban district; in plain view of the Hudson River and the lawns and fields which gently sloped toward the river.

"Mr. Samuel Wood founded the Institution but could not find funding, since it was not a proven fact that the blind could be successfully taught. Dr. John D. Ross came to the school shortly after it was founded and was the superintendent for two years. He invented the phonic alphabet and methods of printing raised characters and maps.

"A few years after the school was founded, it proved to be successful and several wealthy men who refused to help earlier now gave generously. In 1842, there was a description of the school as it appeared in an advertisement, do you see it Darlene?"

"Yes, I have it in my hand."

"Would you read it aloud, I enjoy remembering it's beauty as I hear it read."

> Located in the City of New York, about three miles north of City Hall, upon the block of ground bounded by 33rd and 34th streets and the 8th and 9th Avenues, fronting on the latter and facing the North River.
>
> The building is three stories in height, and is constructed in the modern Gothic style, of Sing Sing marble. It consists of a main or centre building, and two wings, the entire front is 177 feet; length of each wing 125 feet by 25 feet in width.
>
> The building has the capacity for the comfortable accommodation of at least 200 pupils.
>
> A dormitory, hospital, work shops, music and schoolrooms for males are in the northern half of the main or central building; the remainder of the same building and south wing are appropriated for the female pupils in a similar manner.
>
> The dormitories are well ventilated and spacious, being each 25 feet by 125, and under the charge of the respective teachers.
>
> Cold and warm baths, and other essential requisites for health, cleanliness, and comfort, is amply provided. In 1831, a Society was organized in the city of New York, and, on application to the Legislature, was incorporated in the month of April of the same year, by the title of The New York Institution for the Blind.
>
> During class the students would read the *Bible, Pilgrims Progress,The Ancient Mariner* and many other literary classics in raised letters. Selections would be read to the students two or three times and they were expected to answer questions about them in a minute's notice. The following morning they were required to tell the story again in their own words. In this way the students' memories and powers of thinking were greatly enhanced. At breakfast they were read to from the newspapers and in the evenings, many times, students from the nearby seminary would read to them from various books followed by *"Steven's" Travels in the Holy Land.*

Fanny began again, "The school was an oddity for everyone to see, a great conversation piece. People from around the world visited the school when they were in the United States and all American politicians came for a visit. This proved to be good for my future. Because of my skills at poetry, I was asked to write a poem of welcome when someone was scheduled to arrive. Therefore those who visited the Institution came to know me as a child and our relationships would last forever. I am honored to have known every President in my lifetime thus far."

"Aunt Fanny, you seemed to excel at everything, was there anything about school that you didn't like?"

"My favorite studies were English, history, philosophy, and science. Of arithmetic, well…my first lesson consisted of the multiplication tables but you may be sure I was a dull pupil. Two days after this assignment, Dr. Russ came in and said to the girl who was appointed to instruct me, 'Well, Anna, has your pupil learned the multiplication tables yet?' 'Not quite,' she replied. 'Well, then,' said the superintendent, 'I shall come again tomorrow; and if Fanny Crosby does not know them at that time, I shall put her on the mantle.'

"I took his jest in earnest and the next day all of the tables were learned.

"Then we went on as far as long division and there my patience failed. I simply could not learn arithmetic although I tried my best. Finally, in utter despair, I said to my teacher, I suppose you regard me as an inattentive pupil. To my surprise, she replied, 'No, I do not, for you can never learn mathematics. Let us go to the superintendent and tell him.'

"From that hour I was a new creature. What a nightmare I was escaping! I thoroughly appreciated a parody in one of our arithmetics, which runs as follow:

Multiplication is vexation,
Division is as bad,
The rule of three puzzles me,
And fractions make me mad.

"Another time, with my love for poetry, I expressed my feelings for arithmetic:

I loathe, abhor, it makes me sick,
to hear the word, Arithmetic.

"As for singing classes, I loved them. Mr. Anthony Reiff came to teach at the school and remained there for more than forty years. I loved Mr. Reiff as did the other students at the school. Many students looked back to their days at the school and called him the master of their youth.

"On a November morning in 1837 the school laid a corner stone of the new Institution building. The mayor, common council and many prominent people came. I composed a poem and Mr. Reiff put music to it:

This day may every bosom feel
A thrill of pleasure and delight;
It's scenes will in our memories dwell,
When Time shall wing his rapid flight.
"May the great Being who surveys
The countless acts of mortals done,
Behold with an approving eye
The structure, which is now begun.

"In the middle 1800's phrenology was in practice and Dr. Combe of Boston visited the institution to examine the craniums of some of the students."

"Excuse me Fanny, what is phrenology?"

"It is the study of the conformation of the skull as indicative of mental faculties and traits of character."

"Are you telling me that a doctor thought he could tell your personality and mental abilities buy the shape and feel of your skull?"

"Yes, they did believe that and maybe it had some merit. There was a student who said he could listen to two stories, sing a song, and solve a hard problem in mathematics at the same time. When the doctor came to him, he exclaimed, 'Here is a great mathematician.' When Dr. Combe came to look at my head he remarked, 'And here is a poetess; give her every possible advantage. Read the best books to her and teach her to appreciate the best poetry.' At this point Mr. Hamilton Murray, a member of the Board of Managers of the Institution, took me into his charge. My friends knew me as his little protégé. He knew the classics, his natural talents were superior and his knowledge of language was excellent. He read to me from the classics by the hour and advised me to commit long passages to memory."

"Have you kept in contact with many of your friends from the institution?"

Eva told how once, while visiting in Metuchen, New Jersey, a friend came to Fanny and said, "I think we have your old organ at our church." She spoke of a favorite organ on which Fanny used to play at the Institution. At first Fanny could not believe that it was really in existence, she understood that it had been destroyed many years before.

Fanny was overcome with excitement and joined in our conversation.

"They led me to it and said I might finger the beloved keys again, as I had done so many times. It was a rare opportunity and I confess that I shed tears of joy, yet a very sweet feeling took possession of me as I played some of the old melodies that we loved and sang more than sixty years ago. I fancied that time had turned backward and had borne me to those halls again, where I could hear the familiar voices of our pupils singing the classic melodies. There was Mr. Reiff speaking kind words to his scholars; there was our quartet singing before Henry Clay and General Scott; there was Jenny Lind again pouring forth her soul in some Swedish or American patriotic air; Ole Bull again held us spellbound by the touching melodies of his beloved violin; and I thanked the good Father for permitting me to enjoy that happy hour which was indeed the earnest of a happy life.

"Most of the beloved voices of our Institution chorus are now blending with the grand anthem of the Choir Invisible in the great

Tuneful City. But to me they are not hushed forevermore, because I sometimes fancy that I can hear the sweet, low notes of the celestial melodies. Meanwhile, the music of the voices around me here upon this beautiful earth is just as cheerful and inspiring as that I heard in years gone by. Thus life becomes one grand choral song, sweetest at its close; and the tender acts of kindness, strewn all along the way, are the perennial flowers that I have been transplanting and gleaning in the garden of memory for more than ninety summers. As memory rolls back the curtain of the years I behold again the Institution with its spacious halls that ring with mirth and song; its schoolrooms filled with happy hearts and smiling faces; the chapel where morn and eve and Sabbath days we gathered for religious worship; and the beautiful playgrounds, from which the clear sound of the bell called us from our fun to our duty."

"Are there any memories about the school that you would like to forget?"

"Oh, not really. Well, there was one time that I struggled a great deal."

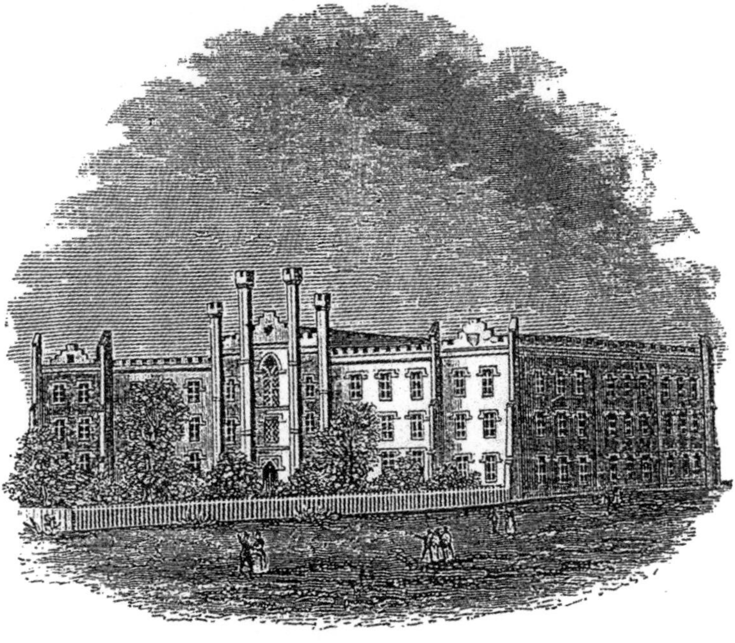

The New York Institution for the Blind

True Test for Fanny

One day Mr. Jones called me into his office, he said, 'Fanny you are not to write a line of poetry for three months.'

"This announcement came to me like a bolt of lightning. I became obsessed with writing poetry. It seemed to be all I wanted to do. Poetry occupied most of my time. For six weeks Mr. Jones enforced his command to the very letter, after which I fell into a state of listlessness.

"My teachers noticed that my lessons were unlearned. I was called to Dr. Jones office again. 'Fanny, what is the trouble with your lessons? Are you ill?'

"I replied, I find it impossible to keep my mind on my lessons, for poetry occupies my thoughts in spite of all efforts to think of other things. I cannot help it.

"Mr. Jones replied, 'Well, write as much as you like, but pay a little more attention to your morning lectures.'

"By 1840 my friends began to spoil me with their praises of my poetry. Superintendent Jones thought something should be done. He called me to his office. It was an impressive occasion. I remember what Mr. Jones said almost word for word: 'Fanny, I am sorry you have allowed yourself to be carried away by what others have said about your verses. True, you have written a number of poems of real merit, but how far do they fall short of the standard you might attain. Shun a flatterer, Fanny, as you would a viper; for no true friend would deceive you with words of flattery. Remember that whatever talent you possess belongs wholly to God and that you ought to give Him the credit for all you do.'

"Mr. Jones was a fine teacher and I knew he was doing what was best for me.

"He continued, 'Now, we will reconstruct the fabric, but on a different plan. You have real poetic talent yet it is crude and undeveloped; and if your talent is ever to amount to much, you must polish and smooth your verses so that they may be of more value. Store your mind with useful knowledge and the time may come, sooner or later, when you will yet attain the goal toward which you have already made some progress. Fanny, have I wounded your feelings?'

"I said, 'No, sir. On the contrary, you have talked to me like a father, and I thank you very much for it.' In years to come I found his words to be worth more than the price of rubies; for a single word, if spoken from the heart, may be just enough to drive another from a dangerous error.

"Later Mr. Jones came to me and said that the school would be sending some of the students on a summer recruiting trip. He would like me to be one of those students. I was excited, I had always dreamed of traveling."

Flo joined us on the porch and said, "May I tell this?"

"You may," answered Fanny.

Summer Recruiting Tours

Flo began her story; the students traveled on the Erie Canal, a chartered boat would serve as their floating hotel. In the summer of 1842 the Board of Managers decided that twenty pupils would tour the central part of New York State to promote the Institution. They wanted parents to know about the school.

The boat would tie up in a town, give an exhibition at the town hall in the evening and in the morning they would move on.

The meetings were opened with a welcome, then the pupils would show their knowledge in reading from raised letters, geography, history, arithmetic and singing. Last Fanny would recite one of her poems.

Fanny began with her poem as if it were the day she first recited it:

"Contented, happy tho' a sightless band
Dear friends, this evening we before you stand;
We for a moment your attention claim
And trust that boon will not be asked in vain.

The varied scenes the rural landscape yields,
The smiling meadows and the flowery fields,
The boundless Ocean and the vaulted skies
Must never, never glad these sightless eyes.

But there's a lamp within, whose sacred light,
Burns with a lustre ever pure and bright
'Tis education, we have shown to you
What by its rays illumed, the blind can do.

Without it, life a dreary waste would be,
With naught to break its long monotony
No sunny beams to light our cheerless way
Our vacant thoughts, ah! whither would they stray.

But thanks to God, his sovereign care we own,
He hath not left us friendless and alone,
His pitying eye beheld the helpless blind
And reared us friends affectionate and kind.

Fain would I bear you to our happy home
Come then with me, on fancy's pinions roam,
Where peace and love, twin sisters, fondly smile,
And music's strains our cheerless hours beguile.

When fair Aurora from the orient sky
Bids night's celestial orb before her fly,
We hail the opening day with vigor new,
And with delight our various tasks pursue.

But oh, while thus our moments sweetly glide.
We think of those like us of sight denied
Whose minds, enshrouded in a mental night.
Sigh to behold instruction's glorious light.

Perchance some tender parent now is here
Whose only child, perhaps a daughter dear,
Of sight bereaved, doth tears of pity claim,
Then why at home that darling one detain.

Place, I entreat you, place your offspring there
Where she, the blessing we enjoy may share;
Where pruned by education's culturing hand
Her intellect, long dormant, may expand.

And she will bless you with affection's tears
When she to you returns in after years
Will with her fingers trace the sacred page
When o'er you steals apace declining age."

"Amazing," I said, "your memory is so sharp!"

"I composed this poem for our tour through the western part of the State of New York in August, 1842. Although I would not have a spiritual rebirth until 1850, this poem still revealed my faith and hope for a better life."

"This travel must have been so exciting to you."

"I had dreamed of traveling from my childhood. One of the most thrilling moments was when at last we arrived at Niagara, where nature has composed her mightiest poem. The grandeur of the surroundings inspired within my heart a reverence such as nothing else in the world has ever awakened; and when we again visited the enchanted spot in the following summer my joy was increased. I could picture it all in my imagination.

"Across the gorge were the woods and fields of the Canadian shore; almost at our feet was that tremendous mass of water plunging directly downward and dashing itself on the rocks one hundred and sixty feet below. Above the falls hung a delicate mist in the sunlight that reflected the countless colors of both earth and sky. While I stood there, completely lost amid the marvelous works of God, Mr. Murray requested me to repeat a poem that had been composed during the previous summer; and while I said over my humble lines we lifted our hearts in thankfulness to the kind Father of us all,

Who spread'st the azure vault above,
Whose hand controls the boisterous sea."

"You talk about these memories as if it were happening today. It must have been a wonderful time."

Fanny smiled and then her voice took on a more serious sound.

"This was a wonderful time, but there would soon come another time with memories I would like more than anything to forget. It was the cholera!"

Summer Tour on Canal Boat

The Dreaded Disease of Cholera, New York and the Institution

The cholera epidemic arrived by passenger ship. On December, 1848, in New Orleans, where 3,500 people died. It then spread all over the United States. By autumn of 1848, the dreaded disease, Asiatic cholera, swept all over Europe slaying thousands and putting the inhabitants of the infected cities into a panic.

"That winter was favorable to the spread of cholera; a mild, damp, muggy atmosphere prevailed, and the physicians in our city began to predict that we were certain to be visited by the terrible scourge within the year. I remember well the spring of 1849. For many months, while the black cloud seemed to be hanging over the defenseless towns of America, we hoped that we might be spared from its ravages but I think the cholera reached New York in March or April of 1849. At first it was confined to the lower part of the city where the authorities tried vigorously to stamp it out, meanwhile endeavoring to keep the matter as quiet as possible for fear of unduly alarming the people."

"I must ask. Did it come into the school?"

"One morning in June, Mr. James F. Chamberlain came running into the office; he was so disturbed that the staff thought something dreadful had occurred. He said to me, 'Will you promise not to tell what has happened?' I told him yes. Then he told the story of how a man came to the Institution and became ill while he was there. The man was taken to the nearest hospital but he died on the way.

"We knew the disease could enter the school at any time. We feared that many of the students might be afflicted and die since none of them had gone home yet for summer vacation. On the following Monday we saw our first case. One of the youngest girls was taken; she called me to her and asked me to hold her in my lap, as I was accustomed to do. 'Miss Crosby, I am going home,' she said, 'and I just wanted to bid you good-bye and to tell you I love you. Now lay me down again.' Toward evening she died and before sunrise the next morning we carried her to Trinity Cemetery where a brief prayer was said; and then, just as the dawn was coming across the eastern hills, our little company slowly wended its way back to the Institution to await the next case.

"Dr. J.W.G. Clements was one of the most skillful physicians that the city afforded but medicine was almost powerless to check the ravages of cholera, except it were used merely as a preventative. I assisted as a volunteer nurse and helped the doctor make some of the remedies. One of them was composed of three parts mercury and one part opium, rolled into pills. I remember that we made six hundred in one day. At the appearance of anything like a symptom of cholera we administered generous doses of these pills, which proved to be efficient remedies in half of our twenty cases, ten terminating fatally."

"It must have been horrible! I can't even begin to imagine."

"It was horrible for everyone who lived through it!" she said. "I shudder when I recall those days; for frequently the stillness of the night, while I was watching at some bedside, would be broken by the hoarse cry. 'Bring out your dead!' the city officials called out as they knocked at the door of a bereaved household. Once, as I was entering the sick room, I struck my foot against an object which I instantly recognized as a coffin awaiting the morning burial.

"When the fourth of July came Dr. Clement and Mr. Chamberlain insisted that I was to go to Brooklyn for a short rest. At the end of three days I was summoned back to the Institution to welcome, with the customary poem, the great Irish temperance advocate, Father Mathew. The brief sojourn of the grand old man in our midst was like the visit of an angel to a house of death. 'Daughter, are you from Ireland?' he asked after I warmly praised the deeds of his countrymen in their struggle for independence.

'No, I was obliged to reply, but I love Ireland.

"Then the kind patriarch of temperance laid his hand reverently on my head and his touch seemed to me like that of a saint who was permitted to leave his abode in heaven for one single moment to cheer the desolate children of earth.

"Not many days after his visit I felt some of the symptoms of cholera myself. During the day I walked about a great deal and took a large quantity of the cholera pills for I was well aware that yielding to the disease practically meant death. Yet I did not tell any of those around me, lest I should frighten them but I excused myself at six o'clock saying that I had been several nights almost without sleep. After a good night's rest I awakened at eight the following morning to find myself in perfectly normal health. When, however, it became known that I had been in danger of the disease there was a hasty consultation after which, Mr. Chamberlain announced that I was to leave for the country on the first of August. So I left the sorrowing city which was almost depopulated by the departure of all who could possibly retire to a safer place until the frosts of November should kill the epidemic."

"Were there any cases after you left?"

"Yes, there were two at the Institution but about two weeks later the twenty pupils who remained were taken to Whitlockville, New York, for the rest of the summer. In late October the mayor of New York wrote a beautiful letter asking his scattered people to return to their homes because the danger was past. So, early in November, the Institution's little family were again united."

"It must have been hard to see how God would get glory out of something like this. Aunt Fanny, how did you keep your faith and how did this event change your life?"

“I began to think more about death during the cholera epidemic. Death became a reality to me. I began to wonder why God would allow something so horrible to happen.”

Fanny's Conversion Experience

My very soul was flooded with a celestial light. I sprang to my feet shouting hallelujah! That's how I remember November 20, 1850.

"Back in 1839, I had been attending the class-meetings at the Eighteenth Street Methodist Church. Some of the teachers used to go down there regularly and on Thursday evenings a leader came to conduct a class in the Institution.

"I was timid and never spoke in public when I could avoid it. The Cholera epidemic caused me to grow indifferent to the means of grace; in fact, I attended the meetings and played the organ for them on the condition that they not call on me to speak. One evening the leader brought a young man with him who would have an important influence on my life. He was Mr. Theodore Camp, a teacher in the city schools and a man known for his generosity. From the beginning of our friendship I found him a true friend.

"In 1845, he was placed in charge of the Institution's industrial department and we began to attend the class meetings together. Mr. Camp never urged me in religious matters and yet I owe my conversion to that same friend, in so far as I owe it to any mortal. By a strange dream I was aroused from a comparative state of indifference. Not that the dream had any particular effect in itself except as the means of setting me to thinking. It seemed that the sky was cloudy for a number of days and finally someone came to me saying that Mr. Camp desired to see me at once. I entered the room and found him very ill.

"Fanny, can you give up our friendship?" he asked.

"No, I cannot; you have been my advisor and friend and what could I do without your aid?"

"But," replied he, "why would you chain a spirit to earth when it longs to fly away and be at rest?"

"Well," I replied, "I cannot give you up of myself but I will seek Divine Assistance."

"But will you meet me in Heaven?" once again asked Mr. Camp.

"Yes, I will, God helping me." I replied.

"And I thought his last words were 'Remember you promised a dying man.'

"Then the clouds seemed to roll from my spirit, and I awoke from the dream with a start. I could not forget those words, 'Will you meet me in Heaven?' and, although my friend was perfectly well, I began to consider whether I could really meet him, or any other acquaintance in the Better Land if called to do so.

"Weeks went by. I had suffered through many of my friends and students dying in the cholera epidemic of 1848. This set me thinking of that haunting question, 'Will you meet me in heaven?'

"In the autumn of 1850, revival meetings were being held at the Thirteenth Street Methodist Church. Some of the staff went down every evening and, on two occasions, I sought peace at the altar but did not find the joy I so craved, until the evening of November 20, 1850.

"It seemed to me that the light must indeed come then or never, so I arose and went to the altar alone. After a prayer was offered, they began to sing the grand old consecration hymn, *Alas, and did my Saviour bleed...And did my Sovereign die?*

"When they reached the third line of the fourth stanza, *Here Lord, I give myself away,* my very soul was flooded with a celestial light. For the first time I realized that I had been trying to hold the world in one hand and the Lord in the other. I realized that I must surrender my whole self over to God, to allow Him to do His work through me they way He wanted to. Not the way I wanted!

"That evening I met Jesus as my own personal Savior. I realized that even though I had always been a good person, even though I was a world famous poet that was not enough. I must trust Jesus Christ to be in control of my life.

"I made a complete surrender of my will; and then I promised to do my duty whenever the dear Lord should make it plain to me. Not many weeks later Mr. Stephen Merritt asked me to close one of our class meetings with a brief prayer. My first thought was 'I can't;' then the voice of conscience said, 'But your promise;' and from that hour I believe I have never refused to pray or speak in a public service with the result that I have been richly blessed."

"Aunt Fanny, was there a special hymn written for your conversion experience?"

"I would write many hymns to describe the joy of my salvation. The one that stands out the most to me right now is this one."

Fanny began to sing in a beautifully trained soprano voice:

Redeemed how I love to proclaim it!
Redeemed by the blood of the Lamb;
Redeemed through His infinite mercy,
His child and forever, I am.

Redeemed, redeemed, Redeemed by the blood of the Lamb;
Redeemed, redeemed, His child, and forever, I am.

Singing with so much anointing Fanny continued and my eyes filled to overflowing with tears.

Redeemed and so happy in Jesus,
no language my rapture can tell;
I know that the light of His presence
With me doth continually dwell.

Redeemed, redeemed, redeemed by the blood of the Lamb,
Redeemed, redeemed, His child and forever I am.

I think of my blessed Redeemer,
I think of Him all the day long,
I sing, for I cannot be silent
His love is the theme of my song.

Redeemed, redeemed, redeemed by the blood of the Lamb,
Redeemed, redeemed, His child and forever I am.

I know I shall see in His beauty
The King in whose law I delight
Who lovingly guardeth my footsteps,
And giveth me songs in the night."

Redeemed, redeemed, redeemed by the blood of the Lamb,
Redeemed, redeemed, His child and forever I am.

"Do you know that one?" Fanny asked

"Oh yes, I do!" My voice could no longer hide the tears I was holding back. She moved forward in her chair to get closer.

"Are you a Christian, Darlene? I do not mean do you go to church? Do you know Jesus Christ as your own personal saviour? Does He dwell within you? Does He own your life? Does He have control of what He owns? Will you meet me in heaven?"

I could see this was important to Fanny. It was her message in life. This was her ministry. It was true she was a famous poet and hymn writer but her personal ministry was leading souls to the Lord. I remembered reading that she wanted to win one million souls to Christ before her death. It was not a game. This was real to Fanny. I was sitting before one of the greatest Christians that ever lived and I wanted to be honest with her.

"Yes, I will meet you in heaven. Yes, I am a Christian. Yes, I do know Jesus Christ as my personal savior. Yes, He does dwell within me. Yes, He does own my life."

The next question was giving me problems. I didn't want to lie to Fanny. "He does not control everything. He does most of the time."

"Most is not enough!" Fanny said, "He wants it all."

"I know. I'm working on it! It's not easy! I struggle with giving all pieces of my life. I have to pray daily to give up some parts of my life!"

"We all do, the main thing is that you try. Let me tell you a little more about that song." Fanny continued. "The Lord does indeed guard my footsteps for during my life I have walked through many treacherous valleys and high mountain peaks in both my spiritual and physical walk.

Who lovingly guardeth my footsteps.
And giveth me songs in the night.

"Many of my songs were written late at night, usually in the wee hours of the morn when most were sound asleep. I have always said that night and day are pretty much the same to me and I didn't need a schedule ruled by the sun."

I could see that Fanny was devoted to making sure of others' futures. It was so important for her to ask every person, "Will you meet me in heaven?" Fanny understood that is was not only her, it is all of us who have fallen short of the Glory of God.

"You know," she said, "we must all call upon His name, He is calling all of us to Him. That is why I wrote these words:

Jesus is tenderly calling thee home,
Calling today, calling today,
Why from the sunshine of hope wilt thou roam?
Farther and farther away.

Calling today, calling today,
Jesus is calling, He's tenderly calling today.
Jesus is calling the weary to rest,
Calling today, calling today,
Bring Him thy burdens and thou shalt be blest.
He will not turn thee away.

Calling today, calling today,
Jesus is calling, He's tenderly calling today."

Fanny told how she shared with the world the greatest and most famous expression of her security in the Lord on a day in 1873 when her girlfriend, Phoebe Knapp, visited her. Phoebe's husband Joseph was one of the founders of the Metropolitan Life Insurance Company.

"We visited a while then Phoebe sat at the piano, 'I wrote this tune Fran,' Phoebe said, 'What does the music say to you? Do you hear any words?'

"I closed my eyes and rocked with the music.

Blessed Assurance, Jesus is mine
Oh, what a foretaste of Glory Divine,
Heir of salvation, purchase of God,
Born of his spirit, washed in his blood,

This is my story; this is my song,
Praising my Savior, all the day long;
This is my story; this is my song,
Praising my Savior all the day long.

Perfect submission, perfect delight,
Visions of Rapture now burst on my sight,
Angels descending, bring from above,
Echoes of mercy, whispers of love.

This is my story; this is my song,
Praising my Savior, all the day long;
This is my story; this is my song,
Praising my Savior all the day long.

Perfect submission, is at rest,
I in my Savior, am happy and blest,
Watching and waiting, looking above,
Filled with His goodness, lost in His love.

This is my story; this is my song,
Praising my Savior, all the day long;
This is my story; this is my song,
Praising my Savior all the day long.

"This is my story, I found that Blessed Assurance. Jesus is mine, Jesus is truly mine and of that I have no doubt. The day that I found Jesus Christ was the happiest day of my life! Oh, what a foretaste of Glory Divine.

"I know without a doubt that I am an heir of salvation, purchase of God, born of his spirit, washed in His Blood, I have given myself over to God completely.

"Perfect submission, perfect delight, I received sight for the first time in my life, a spiritual sight, and now visions of rapture now burst on my sight.

"Angels descending, bring from above, echoes of mercy, whispers of love. I speak of angels often in my songs, whether I actually ever see them no one will never know.

"I am submitted and at rest in my life. Perfect submission, all is at rest.

"I in my Savior am happy and blest There is no doubt that I am blessed.

"I have spent my life preparing and helping others prepare for the wonderful day when Jesus will come for His own. Watching and waiting, looking above, filled with His goodness, lost in His love.

This is my story, this is my song,
Praising my Savior, all the day long.

"It was when I truly gave myself totally to the Lord that He did His greatest work."

"I know that you are right, I will try harder," I promised.

Florance interrupted, "It's time for lunch."

"Lunch already, what time is it?"

Henry chimed in as he took Aunt Fanny's hand and led her indoors, "Half past noon. You must be hungry, thirsty for sure, with all the talking you two have been doing."

Arriving at a beautifully set table I was amazed at the care Flo and Henry put into our lunch. They wanted Fanny's visitor to have a delightful time and I certainly did.

After the meal we went into the parlor. I was shown a picture of Fanny's sister, Mrs. Carrie W. Rider. Fanny and Carrie lived together on State Street in Bridgeport from 1900 until 1906. Because of Carrie's failing health she and Fanny had come to live with Florance and Henry. Florance continued with the photo album of Fanny's life. How interesting for me, there were pictures I had never seen through all of my research.

We visited for a while then I asked Fanny to tell me more about Carrie.

"She and sister Julia were much younger than me, having been born during mother's second marriage. They were always excited and waiting in anticipation to my homecomings and the stories I would have to tell. Julia married Mr. Athington; they had a daughter, Mrs. Leschon. Julia's husband, Mr. Athington was wounded in the civil war."

The Civil War! I had forgotten. Why, these people lived through the Civil War!

"Enough for today, Aunt Fanny needs her nap since she is up with the owls all night long!" Eva stated.

"Eva," Fanny called, "I have told Darlene about your diary and that she may question you concerning me."

A cab was called and off we went. Eva and I spent the afternoon touring downtown Bridgeport. "Have you enjoyed your time with Aunt Fanny?" she said.

"I have. More than you could ever know. May we go back again?"

"Yes, I promised Fanny to bring you back tomorrow."

"You mentioned that Fanny was up with the owls at night. Does that mean she has trouble sleeping?"

"On the contrary! Fanny sleeps in the afternoon and does most of her hymn writing during the night hours. It is quieter and she is left alone to think and listen."

Revival, the Civil War and the Country Fanny Loved

It was morning and I could hardly wait to get back to my newly found friend.

Soon we were sitting on the porch. There we were, Aunt Fanny, Flo, Eva, myself and this time we were joined by Henry.

"Why, Henry," Fanny said. "To what do we owe this honor?"

Henry snickered and just sat there with a grin on his face. He was tall, thin and distinguished. I discerned that he was a gentle kind man. A man who placed concern for others before his own.

"Aunt Fanny," I said, "tell me about the Civil War. What was it like? Were you involved? What did you think about the war?"

"Involved," Henry said, "there is nothing that Aunt Fanny is not involved in."

"Hold on there," she began. "there were two major events in our country that took place at almost the same time."

Fanny began speaking.

"From 1858 to 1860 newspapers were claiming that 50,000 conversions were taking place every week throughout the country. Prayer meetings were springing up everywhere, people were witnessing openly and knocking on doors.

"In 1857 revival broke out in New York City and other parts of the country. So much so that the newspapers were writing about the conversion experiences daily.

"For a preacher to speak on politics or books other than the Bible was wrong!"

Henry interrupted again, "And it was well known to the Pastors that when Fanny Crosby was in their midst, they had better preach the gospel or they would have an uninvited guest as early as the next morning. She would ask the question, 'Whom do you serve, God or man?'"

"But Henry," Fanny joined in, "you know it's true that some preachers try to sneak up on the gospel so quietly they miss it!"

Henry continued, "It was reported that 1,200 people a day were attending the noon meetings at the John Street Methodist Church in New York. Fanny attended the meetings at John Street with Henry Ward Beecher who had become her favorite preacher. Fanny frequently attended at the John Street Church, as well as the Plymouth Congregational Church in Brooklyn to hear Beecher preach."

Fanny took up the conversation, "I also went to the Fifth Avenue Presbyterian Church, to hear Pastor John Hall, the Fourth Avenue Presbyterian Church, for Pastor Howard Crosby (our cousin), the Trinity Episcopal Church and the Dutch Reformed Church on 23rd Street. The Pastor at the Dutch Reformed Church was the Rev. Peter Stryker who introduced me to Mr. William B. Bradbury. Together Mr. Bradbury and I wrote the extremely popular song *There is a Sound Among the Forest Trees,* used during the Civil War. After the war I asked Mr. Bradbury, 'What are you going to do with Forest Trees?' 'What can we do with it?' he asked. 'Oh,' I replied, 'we can write sacred words to the melody; and indeed the subject comes to me now: *There's A Cry from Macedonia.*' With his permission I composed a missionary hymn that was very popular for many years.

"Now, how did I feel about the civil war? I was on the side of the north. In the midst of the revival war broke out and my patriotism was strong. When I believe in something I am strong to defend it and the war was no different. I began to write patriotic songs. Let me share a few lines of one of them.

Death to those whose impious hands
Burst our Union's sacred bands,
Vengeance thunders, right demands
Justice for the brave."

"Now, Aunt Fanny, it would probably be good for you to stop there. Some of the poems you wrote at that time were a little bold!" Henry said.

"I was at a dinner table at a restaurant, in the Savoy Hotel, one time and my tiny flag was pinned on my waist. A southern woman sitting near by exclaimed: 'Take that dirty rag away from here.' Instantly I aroused, and I spoke in no unmeasured terms to her. 'Repeat that remark at your peril.' The manager of the restaurant, who knew me well, came to see what the matter was. I told him what the woman said; he joined me in my condemnation and told her to finish her dinner, pay her bill, leave the restaurant and never enter the place again."

I smiled at Flo who took Henry's chair as he went inside chuckling and shaking his head in amusement.

Fanny continued;

OUR COUNTRY

"Our country, unrivaled in beauty,
And splendor that cannot be told,
How lovely thy hills and thy woodlands,
Arrayed in the sunlight of gold.
The eagle, proud king of the mountain,
Is soaring majestic and free;
Thy rivers and lakes in their grandeur
Roll on to the arms of the sea.

Our country, the birthplace of freedom,
The land where our forefathers trod,
And sang in the aisles of the forest
Their hymns of thanksgiving to God.
Their bark they had moored in the harbor,
No more on the ocean to roam;
And there in the wilds of New England
They founded a country and home.

Our country, with ardent devotion,
On God may thy children abide;
In Him be the strength of the nation,
His laws and His counsel to guide.
Our banner-that time honored banner-
That floats in the ocean's bright foam,
God keep it unsullied forever,
Our standard, our union, our home.

A TRIBUTE

(To the memory of our dead heroes)

To arms! to arms! We remember well
That wild, tumultuous cry,
When our country rang with clash and clang
Of swords that were lifted high;
For the king of war, on his fiery steed,
Shot flames from his flashing eye.

The eagle screamed as he flapped his wings,
And soared to his rock-girt nest,
And the ocean moaned, as he heard the sound
Far, far on his heaving breast.

To arms! to arms! and defend your cause!
In the cannon's boom was heard;
And the clarion swelled its pealing note,
Till every soul was stirred;
And our gallant brave from the homes they loved
Went forth at their country's word.

Side by side on the battlefield,
With loyal hearts and true,
Side by side they fought and died
For the old red, white and blue.

And now we stand on the sacred spot,
Where they laid them down to sleep;
And we touch the cord of memories harp,

And linger awhile to weep.
With grateful hearts and reverent lips,
We tell of their deeds of fame;
And cover them over with fair young flowers
That whisper their honored name.

Their work is done; and from year to year
We hallow their graves anew;
Their work is done, and our banner bright
Unfurled in the breeze we view;
And we look with pride on the Stars and Stripes,
That were saved by the boys in blue."

"My thought about our country is that it will never rise above the level of its home life. We must safeguard that. If we give up on the home for club-life and society, we shall lose all that is best. The nation will crumble if it does not rest in good Christian homes. I know nothing truer than that scene in the poem of Burns, **The Cotters' Saturday Night,** where the father gathers his children about him for prayer and the scripture. No education or culture can take the place of that.

"I believe in God, therefore, cannot believe that the old-fashioned American home with Christ and the family altar in it is doomed."

"It is so good to meet someone who loves her country!" I said. I felt so proud, I wanted to give her a standing ovation!

"You know Aunt Fanny, much has been written about your public life but not much is known about your private life. Do you mind answering some questions?"

"Ask, I will answer as I can otherwise I will have no trouble saying it is none of your business." Fanny answered.

I secretly chuckled while looking at Flo. So much determination, such strong opinions out of such a tiny thing!

Flo said, "Aunt Fanny doesn't talk much about her private life. May I share a little?"

"You may," Fanny answered, "just remember I am listening."

Fanny Crosby as a young lady.

Private Life

Flo began. "After the summer vacation of 1843 touring for the Institution, Fanny's health began to decline and her teachers became alarmed. Dr. Clements knew of her trouble. At first he said that she must not work out of school hours, then he refused to allow her to hear any classes and finally decided to send Fanny into the country to rest a while during the summer of 1844. She insisted that she needed to finish her book first."

Fanny interrupted, "Many of the verses in **The Blind Girl and Other Poems** were autobiographical. The opening lines of the book are:

Her home was near an ancient wood,
Where many an oak gigantic stood;
And fragrant flowers of every hue
In that sequestered valley grew.

A church there reared its little spire,
And in their neat and plain attire,
The humble farmers would repair
On Sabbath morn to worship there.

With their laugh the woodland rang,
Or if some rustic air they sang,
These rural notes of music sweet
The woodland echoes would repeat."

Flo and I smiled at each other and Flo continued; "Fanny wrote three more books, **Monterey, and other Poems** in 1849, **A Wreath of Columbia's Flowers** in 1858 and **Bells at Evening** in 1897. In the foreword for her book **Bells at Evening** Dr. Robert Lowery describes Fanny in this way. Let me read it to you.

> She has a host of friends and she is loyal to those who have proved their friendship. She quarrels with none but she is quick to defend a friend who is attacked. She never forgets a favor but she takes no revenge for a wrong done to her. It is her nature to be confiding and a suspicion once aroused becomes painful to her. She takes it for granted that the world is honest for she sees no reason why it should be otherwise.
>
> She is contented with the things that she has and carries the sunshine of a quiet mind wherever she goes. The cheerfulness of her childhood remains with her and her presence is a rebuke to every form of misanthropy. She takes pleasure in a lively story and is ready to sympathize in a case of distress.
>
> Her nervous temperament keeps her continually on the alert but, when occasion requires, she can retire within herself and be oblivious to all her surroundings. As has already been intimated, Fanny Crosby does not mourn over the fact that she is blind. On the contrary, the writer of this sketch has frequently heard her say that if the gift of sight were offered her she would choose rather to remain blind as she is.
>
> She is firmly of the opinion that her blindness has proved a blessing. If she had not been deprived of sight, she should never have received so good an education, nor have cultivated so fine a memory, nor have been able to do good to so many people. This is her consolation and joy.

Fanny joined in, "Four years after I first entered the Institution Mother remarried. A little sister, Wilhelmina, came into their home but the angel of death soon called her away to that other home above. The letter that I wrote to my mother and step-father enclosed a poem.

Left to right; Mercy, Carrie, Jule and Fanny

Dearest Mother,

The impression that her death has made upon my mind is a deep one but this event teaches me a lesson which, I trust, I never shall forget. Once I looked forward to future years when she would be not only a comfort to you but also to myself but these fond hopes are blighted. Let us not repine, but cheerfully submit to the will of Heaven.

She's gone, ah yes, her lovely form
Too soon has ceased to bloom,
An emblem of the fragile flower
That blossoms for the tomb.
Yet, mother, check that starting tear,
That trembles in thine eye;
And thou, kind father, cease to mourn
Suppress that heaving sigh."

Eva joined the small group gathering on the porch of 226 Wells Street. She said, "Wilhelmina is buried with Mercy at Mountain Grove Cemetery, here in Bridgeport. Mercy (Crosby) and Thomas Morris would go on to have two more daughters. Julia, who they called Jule, and Carolyn, who they called Carrie. They were much younger than Fanny and they admired their big sister."

Fanny laughed and then began to talk. "My two little sisters were always in ecstasy whenever I came home. They saved up their pennies for weeks that they might buy me some sweetmeats. And such chattering: there was so much important news to be told and so many questions on both sides that required immediate answers. Too soon would come the end of these summer outings and my heart always trembled when the hour of parting arrived for I could hear in the distance, as the carriage bore me away, the plaintive voices crying 'Fanny, Fanny, come back!' More than once the old homesickness returned and I was again sorely tempted to turn back from the journey to New York. But it is a rare blessing that these dear sisters have been spared so that the reality of the present is no less gracious than the memory of the past. The days of childhood are recalled as a benediction and the daily ministry of the present is a true manifestation of the love between those who are near and dear to me."

On March 2,1858, Fanny left the institution to begin her new life. Of leaving the school she said, “My parting from those familiar surroundings was indeed sad; for I had been there nearly twenty-three years, eight as a pupil, and fifteen as a teacher. At this point I had written no hymns but had several poetry books published entitled, **The Blind Girl and Other Poems** in 1844 and Monterey and Other Poems in 1851. Other books published after I left the school were; **Bells at Evening** in 1897, **A Wreath of Columbia’s Flowers** in 1897, **Memories of Eighty Years** in 1906.”

“Aunt Fanny, you have told us of leaving the school but not why you left the school. Was it to pursue your hymn writing?”

“Not really. I could have written my hymns while teaching at the school.”

Flo jokingly interrupted, “Let me tell.”

Henry came scurrying out onto the porch; “I think I can tell it the best!” he chimed in.

Fanny said, “I can tell this just fine...”

Fanny and Alexander Van Alstyne

MRS. VAN ALSTYNE,

better known as

FANNY CROSBY,

The gifted BLIND POETESS, who has composed so many of the favorite hymns that are sung in our prayer meetings and Sabbath schools, will give a

Concert and Recitations

in the

Chapel of the South Church,

Monday Evening, Jan. 15th.

She will be assisted by others, including her husband,

MR. VAN ALSTYNE,

who is an accomplished musician, and who is also blind.

Mrs. Van Alstyne, desiring to do good and at the same time support herself, will devote one-half the proceeds to the poor of our city.

Tickets, 25 cents, at E. A. Lewis' Book Store.

Concert to commence at 8 o'clock. 1—10 5d*

Love Comes to Fanny

On March 5, 1858 I married Alexander Van Alstyne, whom I met when he was just a boy on the School's tour at Oswego, New York. His parents attended one of the meetings to find out about an education for their blind son."

"Are you telling me that Alexander was blind also?"

"Yes, we were both blind."

"It must have been difficult being blind in the 1800's?"

"Others supposed it to be challenging, we did not think it out of the ordinary! Van lost his sight during his childhood so he did know what it was like to have sight. In the evenings he would describe the sunset to me. We had no idea what each other looked like. I never saw the face of my dear beloved Van but I knew every crease on it. When the mind is not impressed by the sight you fall in love with a person for whom they really are! We were just acquaintances until he returned from his college years. Van followed and was impressed by my career as a poetess. I was 38 and Van was 27.

"In 1848, Van was the first pupil of the Institution to enroll at a regular college. His chosen vocation was music but he excelled at Greek, Latin, philosophy, and theology. He received his teaching certificate from Union College, Schenectady, New York, and in

1852 became a music instructor in the Albion, New York public schools. By 1855, he returned to the blind school as a music instructor. He enjoyed my poetry, and I enjoyed his music, thus we soon grew to be very much concerned for each other."

A horse-drawn cab stopped out front. It was Fanny's sister, Jule.

"Well Jule, you are just in time, we are telling about Fanny's love life!" said Henry.

"How far have you gone?" Jule asked.

"We just got them married." Henry said.

"This sounds interesting." said Jule as she joined us on the porch.

Our little throng was growing and everyone wanted to be involved in telling this part of Fanny's life.

Fanny acted indignant but you could tell she loved every minute of it.

Jule began. "After their wedding, Van insisted that in public Fanny Crosby keep her well-known name but in private life she became, Frances Jane Van Alstyne."

Fanny added. "From that point on I signed all legal documents as such. Since married couples were not allowed to both teach at the blind school we decided to pursue other careers so after our marriage Van and I moved to Maspeth, New York. Maspeth is part of Queens. I did at times write under the name, Mrs. Van Alstyne, Mrs. Van and etc. Van and I presented many musical concerts together, he would play and I would sing; part of the proceeds would go to the poor and the rest for our own need. Later on to help support me, Van was the organist in two New York churches. He also taught private vocal and instrumental music."

Just then a friend stopped to visit with Fanny. Flo, Eva, Henry, Jule and I carried our conservation into the house.

Flo began speaking softly. "In 1859 they were blessed with the birth of a child, but lost the baby while she was still an infant.

This was the hardest thing that Fanny and Van would ever face and they never spoke publicly about it. I feel they never got over the loss of their child."

Jule spoke softly. "Van would become a sort of recluse and was never the same."

"How would they have ever raised a child, both being blind?" Everyone looked at me with a quizzical look.

Fanny called us back to the porch. She said, "Well, what did I miss? Let's see; Van...we were talking about Van. He was a firm, trustful Christian and a man whose kindly deeds and cheering words will not be forgotten by his many friends. We were happy together for many years. Alexander Van Alstyne died of asthma on June 18,1902 and for him I wrote this poem.

The winds a carol murmur, soft and low,
While silver stars, that gem the arch of night
In answering tones, repeat the choral strain:
Sleep on, O Minstrel, calm be thy repose;

Pure as thy spirit, guileless as thy heart,
May golden dreams of past and future years,
Of deeds accomplished, laurels nobly won,
Beguile thy slumber with their magic power,

And bear thee onward to the classic vales,
Where thou in thought hast wandered o'er and o'er,
Hast laved thy brow in sweet Arcadian springs,
And caught the music of Apollo's lyre:

Sleep on, O Minstrel, angels guard thy rest,
Till in her chariot drawn by flaming steeds
Comes the fair goddess of the blushing morn,
And in her beauty smiling bids thee wake."

"That is truly beautiful, Aunt Fanny. You must have loved him dearly."

"I did" answered Fanny softly, as though reflecting on their time together.

"When did you move to Bridgeport?" I asked.

Prof. Alexander Van Alstyne

1900

The city of Bridgeport has always had peculiar attractions for me, not only because it has long been the home of most of those who are near my heart by ties of blood but because, also, of the delightful acquaintance of many of her generous citizens. Prior to 1900, therefore, my sisters urged me for some years to give up my residence in New York and thus to consider this city my permanent home.

"To this end they were heartily seconded by my publishers who wished to relieve me, as much as possible, after a busy life, from the care and anxiety to which my life as a hymn-writer necessarily was subjected; and principally to place me under the immediate care of those who were ready and willing to do everything in their power to render me the happiest mortal in the world. But I did not accede to their request until, in 1900, through a serious illness, the good Lord over ruled my objection to what seemed like a partial retirement from active labors; and so in May of that year I bade farewell to my many friends in New York, assuring them that I should visit them frequently, as I believed, in the enjoyment of perfect health."

"Do you have many relatives?"

"You mean here in Bridgeport?"

"Here or anywhere?"

"Flo knows them much better than I."

Flo began, "Aunt Fanny's livng relatives are as follows; her sisters, Mrs. Julia M. Athington; Mrs. Leschon, (sister Carrie's daughter); Step-nieces Laura Frances, now Mrs. William Tait; Florance, Mrs. Henry D. Booth; and step-nephew Albert Morris, who married Miss Clara Hope. She also had cousins in Hartford, Bridgeport, Savannah, Georgia, and New York City."

"I do declare, Flo, you have remembered them all quite well." Fanny laughed.

Fanny (center) With Relatives.

Fanny's 85th Birthday

Fanny told how her old home at the New York Institution always remained dear to her, though most of her classmates and fellow teachers were no longer there to welcome her when she entered its sacred halls.

"I look back with tender emotions and gratitude to the many friends and acquaintances who joined to make the occasion of my eighty-fifth birthday, March 24, 1905, most delightful. They came not only from America but also England and the far-off lands of India and Tasmania. A part of my birthday as has been my custom for over twenty years was spent with the Bigelow and Main Company in New York. In the evening the good people of Bridgeport united in giving me a reception at the First Methodist Church which was followed on the next Sunday evening by an address and impromptu reception at the First Baptist Church. This latter church gave me as a birthday gift a dollar for each year of my life. A friend asked if she could give the following pen-picture of my personal appearance on the evening of my birthday at the reception for the newspaper."

> Miss Crosby wore a most becoming dress of brocaded satin, ashes of roses I believe they call the color, with a white chiffon front and a narrow piping on each side of the vest of pink and black velvet, which was very dainty and pretty. As she walked up the aisle, it was suggested that the audience wave their handkerchiefs; and the effect thus produced was as if a white cloud of doves was fluttering over the heads of all, suggesting to those who know Miss Crosby the peace and good will she sheds abroad upon our hearts by her life of song and of good cheer.

Eva stood up, straightened her skirt and announced it was time to be leaving.

There was a collective sigh.

"Aunt Fanny needs her rest." she said. "We'll be back!"

Now I understood why Eva was Fanny's personal secretary. She was kind, giving and business like but her best quality was to know and do what was best for Fanny.

"Will you be back tomorrow?" asked Fanny. "This is becoming quite a circle of ladies, oh... and you too, Henry."

Everyone chuckled.

"Are you enjoying yourself Aunt Fanny?" asked Eva.

"Oh yes, I love to reminisce about the good old times." she answered.

"Then we will see you in the morning," Eva said as we left the house.

"All the same..." Jule spouted.

"We will put Henry to making lunch while we ladies talk!" Fanny laughed as we walked to our cab.

Over dinner Eva and I talked about our day. "What more can you tell me about the baby?" I asked.

Eva said "Phoebe Knapp once told me that the child was a girl, she died in her sleep."

Instantly I muttered, "SIDS"! Sudden infant death syndrome is what we call it today.

"What was that?" Eva asked.

"Nothing, I was just thinking out loud."

I listened as Eva continued. "Phoebe told how Fanny and Van awoke one morning and realized they had slept in, the baby had not awakened them. They laid their hands upon her chest and found her body lifeless."

"It must have been horrible for Fanny and Van."

"I'm sure it was, Fanny never speaks of it and I am told that Van was never the same. It is Fanny's way never to talk about times of hurt, she deals with her pain through hymn writing. Even though Fanny tells that she wrote the song for Mr. William Howard Doane, Phoebe feels the hymn, *Safe in the Arms of Jesus*, was really written for their baby. It was written in the quiet of her bedroom, on her knees, probably while remembering the feel of her own little baby in her arms?"

"Eva," I said, "please keep in your diary a record of all Fanny's last days. I am sure it will be of great importance someday."

"I think that it is important also and I try to." Eva responded.

As I retired that evening I remembered Fanny said *Safe in the Arms of Jesus* was the most favorite hymn she had ever written. As I sang the words, I heard for the first time the sound of a lullaby, rocking my arms as if holding an infant and thinking of her baby I wept openly, honestly feeling Fanny's pain.

Safe in the Arms of Jesus, Safe on His gentle breast.
There by His love o'er-shaded, sweetly my soul shall rest.

Fanny Crosby with Henry and Florance 1914.

Fanny's Address at Carnegie Hall

"Once again our little group was seated on the porch; Fanny, Jule, Eva, Florance, me and, of course, Henry.

"Jule", I said, "Glad to see you today."

"I spent the night so I could rejoin the group, I wouldn't miss this for the world. I am hearing stories from Fanny that I have never heard before."

"Well, tell me Aunt Fanny, I know that you have spoken many times, what was the most memorable?"

Fanny started. "The year was 1912. I was 91 years old when I brought the house down at an Evangelistic Rally at Carnegie Hall. Eva can you find that news article they wrote."

"It's right here Aunt Fanny."

"Would you read it for us?"

"Certainly!" said Eva.

This is the way the newspaper reported it:

Five thousand persons attended the opening rally of the Evangelistic Committee's seventh annual tent, open air and shop campaign at Carnegie Hall last night and when Fanny Crosby was assisted up to the stage.

The choir of 200 and the audience burst into 'We're Traveling On.' The audience saw a frail and feeble woman when she was first helped to the stage.

But they realized their mistake as soon as it came her turn to speak. Standing firmly, with only the back of a chair to hold for support, she told the evangelical sympathizers in a firm well-pitched voice that she expected to live until she was 103.

This was Fanny's speech, "When I was taken from the carriage into the hotel today, I heard someone say; Get her a rolling chair. But I spoke right up; I don't need any rolling chair. I can walk on my own feet. My strength is in the Lord.

"Oh men of the Empire City, you are dear to my heart.

"This scene takes me back to my twenty-five years of mission work. When I came in and when you greeted me so warmly, I wanted to weep tears of joy. I shall pray for a million souls to be saved and I shall pray until every soul has been gathered up into mercy."

Hymn Stories

"Aunt Fanny, I would like to talk about your hymns today but before we start there is one question that I must ask."

"What might that be?"

"As I have researched hymns I have found several that sound as if you have written them. Written with the same co-writers that you used yet the author is another name. Am I imagining this?"

"On the contrary my dear. You are very perspicacious! I have written under approximately 250 pseudonyms. For a while I was the only writer for the publishing firm of Bigelow & Main. The publishing business is a very large industry and they did not want the other publishers to know they only had one writer on staff."

"Very interesting. What are some of the names?"

"A few of my favorite and most common used were: James Apple, Ella Dale, Lidie Edmunds, Lizzie Edwards, F.A.N., Carrie Frances (mine & my sisters names), Florance Booth (my niece's name), Grace Francis, Jenie Glen, Frances Hope, Mary D. James, Sallie Martin, Sallie Smith, Sam Smith, Mrs. Van and Mrs. Van Alstyne. I wrote under initials, F.C., F.J.C., F.J.V.A., J.V.A., and many more. I even wrote under some symbols like, ##, #*" and ***. I think that is enough for now, I would not want to ruin for you the pleasure of searching for them. Darlene, you remind me a lot of myself when I was younger. I have a feeling that you will find the rest. You must dig deep!"

"I know most of your hymns have been inspired by real life circumstances. Will you share some of those stories?"

She started, "The most enduring hymns are born in the silences of the soul and nothing must be allowed to intrude while they are being framed into language. Some of the sweetest melodies of the heart never see the light of the printed page. Sometimes the song without words has a deeper meaning than the more elaborate combinations of words and music.

"That some of my hymns have been dictated by the blessed Holy Spirit I have no doubt; and that others have been the result of deep meditation I know to be true; but that the poet has any right to claim special merit for himself is certainly presumptuous. I have sometimes felt that there was a deep and clear well of inspiration from which one may draw the sparkling draughts that are so essential to good poetry. At times the burden of inspiration is so heavy that the author himself cannot find words beautiful enough, or thoughts deep enough, for its expression.

"Most of my poems have been written during the long night watches, when the distractions of the day could not interfere with the rapid flow of thought. It has been my custom to hold a little book in my hand and, somehow or other, the words seem to come more promptly when I am so engaged. I can also remember more accurately when the little volume is in my grasp. Many people, noting this peculiar custom, have asked some queer questions about it; and not a few fancy that I may indeed be able to see what is printed there.

"*Blessed Assurance* was written in 1873, to a melody composed by my friend, Mrs. Joseph F. Knapp. She played it over once or twice on the piano and then asked what it said to me. I replied:

Blessed Assurance, Jesus is mine,
O, what a foretaste of glory divine!
Heir of salvation, purchase of God,
Born of His spirit, washed in His blood.
This is my story this is my song,
Praising my Saviour all the day long.

"The hymn thus written seemed to express the experience of both Mrs. Knapp and myself. Phoebe became known to me as early as 1868, and has also written the notes to several hymns of mine, including *Nearer The Cross,* and *Open the Gates of the Temple."*

Jule shared these stories. "During a stay in Cincinnati Fanny and the Doanes enjoyed an evening of conversation. Late that evening upon Fanny retiring she wrote *I Am Thine, 0 Lord.* Another day in 1874, Fanny was wondering how she would pay her rent. She decided she must pray for it. Soon after her prayer a man she did not know placed a $10.00 bill in her hands. It was the exact amount she needed. She then wrote, *All the Way, My Saviour Leads Me.*

Jule continued, "Fanny was visiting William and Sara Kirkpatrick in Germantown, Pennsylvania. A group gathered, they were talking about life itself when Fanny said, 'How soon we grow tired of earthly pleasures, however bright they are.' Fanny surprised everyone when she began to cry. 'But what comes next?' Fanny said. Everyone stopped what they were doing, Fanny said, *'Why Glory to God, Hallelujah!'* Fanny insisted that Mr. Kirkpatrick sit down right then and compose the tune."

We are never weary of the grand old song,
Glory to God, Hallelujah!
We can sing it in the Spirit as we march along,
Glory to God, Hallelujah!

Fanny began to speak again. "Among the great number of hymns that I have written-eight thousand perhaps-it is not always possible for me to remember even the best of them. For this reason I have made laughable mistakes. One morning, for example, at Dr. Moody's place, in Northfield, Massachusetts the audience sang *Hide Me, O My Saviour.* I did not recognize this hymn as my own production and therefore I may be pardoned for saying that I was much pleased with it. Turning to Mr. Sankey, I asked, 'Where did you get that piece?' He paid no particular attention to my question, for he supposed I was merely joking and at that moment the bell called us to dinner so both of us forgot about the hymn. It was again used at the afternoon service and then I was determined to know who wrote it. Mr. Sankey, I said, now you must tell me who is the author of *Hide Me, O My Saviour.* 'Really,' he replied, 'don't you recall who wrote that hymn? You ought to remember, for you are the guilty one.'

"Most of my hymns were from experiences in my own life. *Hold Thou My Hand*, for which Hubert P. Main wrote the music, was one of them. For several days I felt depressed, this was unusual, I was always a happy person. In my weakness I cried out, Dear Lord, hold Thou My Hand. Almost at once the sweet peace that comes of perfect assurance returned to my heart and my gratitude for this evidence of answered prayer sang itself in the lines of the hymn:

Hold Thou my hand, so weak I am and helpless,
I dare not take one step without Thy aid;
Hold Thou my hand, for then, O loving Savior
No dread of ill shall make my soul afraid.

"After the death of the great Charles Spurgeon, his wife wrote for a copy of this poem and said she found comfort from hearing it sung.

"On April 30, 1868, Dr. W. H. Doane came into my house and said, 'I have exactly forty minutes before my train leaves for Cincinnati. Here is a melody. Can you write words for it?' I replied that I would see what I could do. Then followed a space of twenty minutes during which I was wholly unconscious of all else except the work I was doing. At the end of that time I recited the words to

Safe in the Arms of Jesus. Mr. Doane copied them, and had time to catch his train.

"I have often spent three or four hours on half as many lines and then cast them aside as worthless. In composing hymn-poems there are several ways of working. Often subjects were given to me to which melodies must be adapted.

"I have claimed this song as the most favorite one I have ever written:

Safe in the arms of Jesus
Safe on His gentle breast,
There by His love o'er-shaded
Sweetly my soul shall rest.
Hark, tis the voice of angels
Borne in a song for me,
Over the fields of glory
Over the jasper sea.

Safe in the arms of Jesus,
Safe on His gentle breast,
There by His love o'er-shaded,
Sweetly my soul shall rest.

Safe in the arms of Jesus
Safe from corroding care,
Safe from world's temptations
Sin cannot harm me there.
Free from the blight of sorrow,
Free from all doubts and fears;
Only a few more trials,
Only a few more tear.

Safe in the arms of Jesus
Safe on His gentle breast,
There by His love o'er-shaded
Sweetly my soul shall rest.

Jesus, my heart's dear refuge,
Jesus has died for me,
Firm on the rock of ages
Ever my trust shall be.
Here let me wait with patience,
Wait till the night is o'er;
Wait till I see the morning
Break on the golden shore.

Safe in the arms of Jesus,
Safe on His gentle breast,
There by His love o'er-shaded,
Sweetly my soul shall rest.

"My verses come without the slightest effort, as though someone were singing them to me. I retire at night with a theme or a strain of music on my mind; in the morning there is the complete song, stanza by stanza. I have really felt at times that the angels had been talking to me. Thus 'Hark, Tis the Voice of Angels, borne in a song for me.'

"There are a great many beautiful stories connected with this hymn. Ira D. Sankey related a conversation with a simple Scotch woman who came to him after a great meeting.

> 'I want to thank you for writing Safe in the Arms of Jesus:' she said. 'My daughter was fond of it and sang it as she passed to the life beyond.' 'But,' replied the evangelist, 'I did not write the hymn. Fanny Crosby wrote the words and W. H. Doane the music. Sit down, my good woman, and I will tell you about it.' A look of disappointment passed over the dear woman's face, but as she listened to Mr. Sankey's story her countenance again lighted up and she said, 'When ye gang back to America tell Fanny Crosby that an auld Scots woman sends her blessing and her love.'

"The late Dr. John Hall used to tell a touching story of *Safe in the Arms of Jesus.* He went to see the little daughter of a member of his congregation; and her father came downstairs in tears.

'My dear friend,' asked the clergyman, 'What is the trouble? Has the little girl gone home?' 'No,' replied the father, 'But she has asked me to do something that I cannot do; anything that wealth might buy she may have, but I cannot sing *Safe in the Arms of Jesus*, for I never sang a note in my life.' 'Oh,' said Dr. Hall, 'I will go up and sing it for her.' When he reached the last two lines of the hymn, Wait till I see the morning Break on the golden shore, the spirit of the child passed to that land where all shall sing the melodies of Zion.

"Another incident of the singing of *Safe in the Arms of Jesus* was related by a sea captain who was in the habit of holding services on board his vessel. From Sabbath to Sabbath he noticed that there was a certain man who did not unite with the others when they sang that hymn. At last he approached the sailor and inquired if he did not enjoy the meetings. 'Oh, yes,' the latter replied, 'but I am not Safe in the arms of Jesus and I cannot sing that hymn.' The captain prayed with him, and as a direct result of the interview, ere the next Sabbath, the sailor was singing the piece with the rest.

"Some years after the writing of *Jesus, I Love Thee* Mr. Stebbins came to me and said, 'I think I have something both of us will enjoy. I have a melody here, and would like to have you write the words for it while we are together.' He played it over for me and I was pleased with the tune and wrote *They Tell Us of a Land So Fair.* Mr. Stebbins also wrote the music to *Jesus is Calling, No Sorrow There, The Day Star Hath Risen, 0 Sing of My Redeemer* and many others.

"It was a cold, rainy day, and everything had gone wrong with me during the morning. I realized that the fault was my own; but that did not help the matter.

"About noon the sky began to be clear and a friend standing near me said, There is only a beam of sunshine, but, oh, it is warm and bright and, on the impulse of the moment, I wrote the hymn, *Only a Beam of Sunshine.*

Only a beam of sunshine, but, oh, it was warm and bright,
The heart of a weary traveler was cheered by its welcome light.

"One day someone was talking about wealth and he said, 'If I had wealth I would be able to do just what I wish to do and I would be able to make an appearance in the world.'

I replied, *Take the world, but give me Jesus."*

Henry said, "I have heard these stories before, let me share one. On one occasion Mr. Kirkpatrick had been at Fanny's home and as he was going away she said, 'Oh, dear, it's nothing but meeting and parting in this world.' He replied, 'Well, I will not say as Phillip Bliss did, meet me at the fountain, but I will say, where the tree of life is blooming, meet me there.' Not long afterward Fanny wrote the hymn entitled *Meet Me There."*

Fanny picked up the conversation, "During the summer of 1902 I was visiting Dr. William H. Doane when I received a telegram announcing the death of a dear friend. It occurred to me that under the circumstances it would be well for me to occupy my mind by writing as many hymns as I could. I accordingly secluded myself and wrote *I Am Satisfied."*

"Mr. Sylvester Main was a little depressed once and I said that if we were always at peace with God these trials would not annoy us as they do now.

" 'No,' he replied, 'and I often have to exclaim, *Lord abide with me.'* His remark inspired me to write the hymn bearing this title."

"Valley of Eden, Beyond the Sea is one of my hymns of which I have erred concerning the authorship. On one occasion I heard a lady singing it and I rushed downstairs exclaiming, 'Where did you get that beautiful melody and words?'

"Well," she replied, "Mr. Kirkpatrick wrote the melody."

"But," I said, "Who wrote those words?"

She replied, "Someone who is in the habit of writing for him." Even then I did not recognize my own words; and she finally said that she would sing the hymn once more, which she did. To my embarrassment I remembered writing it.

"Dr. Lowry gave me the subject to *The Bright Forever* and I tried for two days to write the hymn. Then all at once, almost in a twinkling, the words came stanza by stanza as fast as I could memorize them."

Henry joined in once again, "I love this story. An English religious weekly gave the following account of how soldiers use *God Be With You* and *Blessed Assurance* for passwords. When one member of the Soldiers' Christian Association would meet a comrade he would say 494 which is the number of *God Be With You Till We Meet Agai*n in **Sacred Songs and Solos;** the latter replied 6 farther on, that is 500, which was the number of *Blessed Assurance.* "Of this custom the secretary of the Association wrote that these hymns are constantly being used by our members as greeting and response and I do not think any member of the Soldiers' Christian Association ever writes without putting them somewhere on the letter or envelope. Fanny has dozens of letters from South Africa alone; and in her visits to garrisons and soldiers' homes no meeting is considered closed until *God Be With You* had been sung."

"Well Henry, we women are working up an appetite. Do you suppose you could put something together?" Fanny said.

"I suppose I can. I will get right to it." Henry answered.

"Aunt Fanny what an interesting life you have led. You could go on forever with stories about your hymns."

"I have written many of them, each with a story! In one of Mr. Sankey's meetings a man came forward and requested that someone offer a prayer for him. He appeared to be deeply distressed in spirit and Mr. Sankey suggested that he might come again the next night. He cried earnestly, 'No, it must be settled tonight; for tomorrow may be too late.' Mr. Sankey listened to his appeal and before he left the church he felt that he was saved. The next day there was an explosion in the mine where he worked and he was among the slain. Mr. Sankey related this story to me and I wrote the hymn *Shall I Be Saved Tonight?"*

Eva began again; "I love the ones with chilling stories like the last. The story of *Pass Me Not, O Gentle Saviour* (1868) was written late one evening. Fanny just returned home from the Manhattan Prison where she had gone with her church group. They were conducting a service and Fanny loved going along. They sang hymns and Fanny's preacher preached; the service ended with an altar call. The room was crowded and men were moving from all directions. All of a sudden there was a voice from the back of the room, one of the prisoners cried out, 'Oh good Lord, please don't pass me by!' There was the answer she had been looking for. She heard the answer to her prayer. 'Do not pass me by!' Several days later Fanny sent the completed lyrics to Mr. Doane. It became one of her best-known hymns that is still being sung today."

Pass, me not O gentle Saviour,
Hear my humble cry,
While on others Thou art calling,
Do not pass me by.

Saviour, Saviour,
Hear my humble cry
While on others Thou art calling,
Do not pass me by.

Let me at Thy throne of mercy,
Find a sweet relief.
Kneeling there in deep contrition,
Help my unbelief.

Saviour, Saviour,
Hear my humble cry,
While on others Thou art calling,
Do not pass me by.

Trusting only in Thy merit,
Would I seek Thy face.
Heal my wounded, broken spirit,
Save me by Thy grace.

Saviour, Saviour,
Hear my humble cry,
While on others Thou art calling,
Do not pass me by.

Thou the spring of all my comfort,
More than life to me.
Whom have I on Earth beside Thee,
Whom in heaven but Thee.

Saviour, Saviour,
Hear my humble cry,
While on others Thou art calling,
Do not pass me by.

Eva continued, "A number of stories have been called forth by the singing of that hymn and perhaps the best is the following. In a Western state lived an old man who was in the habit of going fishing on Sunday afternoons. Near the pond was a small schoolhouse in which was held a Sabbath school. Frequently they used to sing *Pass Me Not* during the afternoon service and for some reason, the old man could not forget that melody. One day he could resist no longer. He threw down his fishing rod and went up to the schoolhouse. They invited him into the Sunday school but he said, 'No, I cannot go in today; for I am not dressed well enough.' He finally promised to enter on the condition that the children should sing *Pass Me Not, O Gentle Saviour.* For more than fifty years he had not darkened the church door but the old memories began to come back again and he could not resist their appeal. Two years later he attended a convention at which Dr. Doane was present, and related the story, concluding with the words, 'God bless William H. Doane and Fanny Crosby!'"

Fanny said, "Sometime after the hymn *Rescue the Perishing* became known I was at a service and a young man told the story of his conversion. Poor and hungry, he walked the streets for want of something better to do. He heard the singing at a mission, he went in and, before the service was concluded, his heart broke in contrition. He told, 'I was just ready to perish but that hymn, by the grace of God saved me.' As I stood there face to face with that young man, the audience was thrilled with the pathos of our meeting for the first time and tears were shed in every part of the room."

Only a little way', said an old lady, who was suffering with pain, as she looked up into the clear blue sky just as the sun was setting. 'Tis only a little way on to my home'. I wrote the hymn bearing that title."

"One afternoon Sylvester Main was humming a melody and I said to him, 'Oh, Mr. Main that is beautiful and, if you will let me I am going to write a hymn for it.'

'Well' he said in his gentle way, 'if you think it is worth it, you may do so.'

I composed *Jesus, I Come to Thee."*

"In the summer of 1894, *Saved by Grace* was used publicly for the first time, but the words had been written and sent to the publishers more than two years previous although they were not set to music. The hymn itself was called into being through a little incident in a sermon preached by Dr. Howard Crosby who was a distant relative and a dear friend of mine. He said that no Christian should fear death for if each of us were faithful to the grace given us by Christ, the same grace that teaches us how to live would also teach us how to die. His remarks were afterward published in a newspaper and they were read to me by Mr. Bigelow. Not many hours after I heard them I began to write the hymn,

Some day the silver cord will break,
And I as now no more shall sing,
But, oh, the joy when I shall wake
Within the palace of the King."

"A friend sent the following story to me, relative to *Saved by Grace.* She and a companion were attending one of the auditorium meetings at Northfield and that hymn was sung. A friend made some remark concerning her acquaintance with Fanny and a lady, who was sitting directly in front of her, happened to catch it. Turning around, she asked eagerly, 'Did I understand you to say that you know the author of *Saved by Grace?'* On being assured that she heard correctly, she continued, 'Will you kindly tell her what this hymn has done for me? Twelve years ago I was assailed by a great temptation at an important crisis in my life and, although I had been a professing Christian, I was on the point of deciding for the wrong course. In this state of mind I entered a little chapel, not so much to hear the sermon as to listen to the sweet singing and, most of all, to think out my own problem. Of the sermon I did not hear one word, but when the soloist began to sing, *I Shall see Him Face to Face*, my heart melted. It seemed that God had spoken to me through the voice of that song and I at once decided to take the right path. Ever since I have felt that the hymn saved me. I have longed to see Fanny Crosby and if you ever meet her, please tell her the story for me.'"

Eva shared a newspaper clipping from Fanny's memoirs. This story actually appeared in an Allegheny, Pennsylvania newspaper.

> The congregation of Christ Protestant Episcopal Church, Allegheny, was startled yesterday by an unusual supplement to the morning service. The reading had been concluded and the rector was about to make the usual announcements when an incident occurred such as old Christ Church had never dreamed of. In the forth pew from the front a neatly dressed woman about thirty years of age rose up, and struggling with emotion began to speak. She was allowed to go on and in clear tones she told of being christened in the church, of attending the Sunday school, of a Godly mother's affection and care and of the instruction received from her.
>
> Then came a story of sin and shame, of years spent in the theatrical profession, and of the folly of such a godless life. She recounted how, two years before that day, while she was on her way to a public park in the city of Chicago, she heard a company of Methodists at an open-air meeting sing *Saved By Grace*. The words and the melody arrested her, recollections of her childhood days were awakened and the memory of her mother's prayers and tears lashed her conscience. Kneeling on the curbstone, she prayed for

pardon and there and then received it. She left the spot with the peace of God in her heart. She gave up her profession at once and for two years had been living a victorious and useful life. She concluded her testimony with words like these: I have not been in this church for many years and I could not resist the impulse to give this testimony. The Lord Himself sent me here.

Some Letters Sent to Fanny

"Eva, do you have your hand on my letters?"

"Yes, I do, I knew where you were heading!"

"Will you please find the one that Mr. Sankey wrote from England the summer of 1900? Also the one from Mr. Faddoul Moghabghab from Syria?"

"I have them." Eva replied.

"Among the many interesting letters I have received, these two bear more directly upon the story of my life. Eva, would you please read them?"

Dear Fanny:

You are not forgotten and your name is often mentioned in connection with Saved by Grace in my services. We are keeping well and are just starting for Leeds, York, Sunderland, Berwick, Newcastle and Edinburgh where large halls have been taken for our meetings. I quoted your beautiful lines of poetry recently in Birmingham:

'Oh, for an angel's harp to tell How much I love Thee and how well'

They are fine and some of our mutual friends have written them down in their Bibles. I hope you are still as bright as a dollar, as you say.

Sincerely yours, Ira D. Sankey.

Miss Fanny Crosby, Most beloved sister in Christ:

I am writing this letter with my Syrian pen and must therefore put the Syrian custom into practice on such an occasion like this. Easter Week, Jesus Christ is Risen, Is risen indeed.' We see these terms in Syria in place of your 'Good morning,' or 'Good evening,' etc., especially on Sunday, Easter-day; and wheresoever we go or with whomever we speak the first salutation is 'Jesus Christ is risen today,' and the reply 'Is risen indeed.'

Sister, though you are still in the body on this earth, you are always quoting the language of Heaven above. Your thoughts are continually discovering new regions beyond the river. Oh, I imagine how happy you always feel and I hope to have another chance of meeting you again upon this earth, because I always gain new inspiration from those whose mansions are already prepared by the 'Shepherd of the Sheep'. I am sure, if we cannot meet each other in this world, we shall meet in Heaven.

I remain, yours in Christ, Faddoul Moghabghab

Business Associates

"Aunt Fanny, you must tell me about the people you wrote with. What were they like? And who..."

"Lunch is ready ladies," Henry announced.

Fanny chimed in, "Where has the day gone? It has been so enjoyable."

After lunch we carried our conversation about Fanny's business associates to the parlor until Eva interrupted and said it was time for Fanny to rest.

"Will I see you tomorrow?" Fanny said.

Eva answered, "Aunt Fanny, we have been at this for 3 days now! Don't you think it is time for a days rest?"

"Nonsense," Fanny said, "I feel an urgency to finish and besides, nothing thrills my soul more than talking about the Lord's workings! Eva try to find the sketches of my business associates tonight, would you please?"

Eva and I made our way back to her place and I retired for the afternoon. I needed time alone to put together my thoughts and the pictures Fanny had given to me. I will now share with you what Fanny had to say about some of these people.

George Root

In 1845, George F. Root came to the Institution to teach music, he was a well known composer of both secular and sacred music. He would play melodies for Fanny and ask her to put words to them. In 1851, he played a tune that was sweet and touching; and Fanny exclaimed, "Oh, Mr. Root, why don't you publish that?"

He told her there were no words for it and he could not purchase any.

To which Fanny suggested that he let her try to write something; he agreed; and she composed a song beginning as follows:

"O come to the greenwood, where nature is smiling,
Come to the greenwood, so lovely and gay,
There will soft music thy spirit beguiling
Tenderly carol thy sadness away."

Their first song was entitled *Fare Thee Well, Kitty Dear.* During the next three years together they would write fifty or sixty secular songs, some of their titles: *Bird of the North, Rosalie, the Prairie Flower, Hazel Dell, They Have Sold Me Down the River, O How Glad to Get Home, Proud World Goodbye, The Honeysuckle Glen,* and *There's Music in the Air.*

In 1853 they wrote what has become known as the first American cantata, *The Flower Queen.* It was an instant success. They went on to write another cantata entitled, *Pilgrim Fathers.*

William Batchelder Bradbury

William Batchelder Bradbury

Rev. Peter Stryker, the minister at the Dutch Reformed Church on Twenty-third Street, a church Fanny frequently attended, arranged a meeting on February 2,1864, between Fanny and William B. Bradbury. His office was at 425 Broome Street. They would meet at the Ponton Hotel on Broom Street for lunch.

Mr. William Bradbury was born in Maine in 1816 and studied music most of his life. He was an organ salesman, selling organs to churches and also the organist for the New York Baptist Tabernacle.

At the age of thirty, Mr. Bradbury went to England and Germany to study music. At the time he met Fanny he was manufacturing Bradbury pianos and was well known as a popular songwriter.

During their first meeting at the Ponton Hotel, to Fanny's surprise Mr. Bradbury said, "Fanny, I thank God that we have at last met for I think you can write hymns and I have wished for a long time to have a talk with you."

At the end of their meeting Fanny promised him a hymn in one week and on February 5th, 1864, she returned with some verses that Mr. Bradbury soon set to music and published as her first hymn, *Our Bright Home Above.*

There were four stanzas; and one of them is as follows:

"We are going, we are going
To a home beyond the skies,
Where the fields are robed in beauty,
And the sunlight never dies;
Where the fount of joy is flowing
In the valley green and fair.
We shall dwell in love together;
There shall be no parting there.
We are going, we are going,
And the music we have heard,
Like the echo of the woodland,
Or the carol of a bird.

The following week Mr. Bradbury sent for Fanny and said that he wanted a patriotic song. The melody that he composed was difficult but Fanny listened to it two or three times and was able to count the measures. She then easily wrote the words. On the following morning she took the song to Mr. Bradbury's office. His bookkeeper, who was also a musical man, played it on the piano, exclaiming, "How in the world did you manage to write that hymn? Nobody ever supposed that you, or any other mortal, could adapt words to that melody."

At that moment Mr. Bradbury came in to the office and, after looking over the hymn carefully, turned to Fanny and exclaimed, "Fanny, I am surprised beyond measure; as long as I have a publishing house, you will always have work." Thus began their four years of hymn writing which would launch Fanny into a very successful career.

Sometimes Mr. Bradbury gave her the titles for hymns to melodies already written but usually she was allowed to make her own selection. A large part of what she did was to revise poems that Mr. Bradbury had already purchased from other authors.

During a period of four years they worked side by side, until, on January 7th 1868, Mr. Bradbury died. Fanny was heart broken. The funeral was hard for her. She heard a voice from behind telling her to go on with Mr. Bradbury's work. She would later claim the voice to be that of their Lord. She remembered her promise, not only to Mr. Bradbury but also to the Lord, to continue His work.

William B. Bradbury is buried in Bloomfield Cemetery, Bloomfield, N.J.

Bigelow & Main Publishing

Sylvester Main

Thirty-five years after Fanny and Sylvester Main had known each other as children in Ridgefield they met once again. It was February 2nd, 1864. Sylvester was a singing teacher and a well-known choir director at Norfolk Street Methodist Church in New York City.

Shortly after the death of Mr. Bradbury, the firm of Bigelow and Main was formed by Sylvester Main, his son Hubert Main, and L. H. Bigelow.

Bigelow and Main hymns were well known in several foreign countries, especially in England. Their publishing house was composed of several musical men. They were all Fanny's friends. Their names were Hubert P. Main, William F. Sherwin, Theodore F. Seward, Henry Tucker, Chester G. Allen, Philip Phillips and Theodore E. Perkins.

Two years before Fanny and Sylvester had met at Mr. Bradbury's office. He had been associated in the publishing business and continued as a member of the firm until his death in 1873. Fanny always found him a faithful counselor and a friend.

His last words were, "The dear Lord is about to give me rest. If you love me, do not weep, but rejoice." Fanny said these words of cheer, coming as the parting message of one whom she loved, in later years came to be a source of inspiration and comfort in many dark times. The words of one of her own hymns, for which his son, Hubert P. Main, wrote the music, recalled sweet memories of him, and many other friends, who await her in the Better Land:

"On the banks beyond the river
We shall meet no more to sever,
In the bright, the bright forever,
In the Summer land of song."

L. H. Bigelow

L.H. Bigelow, the senior member of the firm, continued the publishing business after the death of his partner Mr. Main. For thirty years Mr. Bigelow and Fanny worked together and, during this time, Fanny said never even the slightest misunderstanding arose between them.

Fanny Crosby with Hubert P. Main

Hubert P. Main

Hubert P. Main had known Fanny since 1864. They spent many hours in his music library discussing writing hymns and their melodies. He valued Fanny for her value in criticizing work. Fanny valued Hubert for his knowledge of hymns. Many years he was the accomplished compiler for the Bigelow and Main Company and he set to music some of Fanny's best hymns, including *The Bright Forever, Hold Thou my Hand, Blessed Homeland, The Blessed Rock, Yes, There's Pardon For You,* and many others.

Upon Fanny's retirement, Hubert Main would see to it that she would receive all of the remaining royalties from her book **Bells at Evening.**

Phoebe Knapp

Every woman must have one special lady friend. One to tell your deepest, darkest girlhood secrets.

Phoebe Knapp was that one friend. She was Fanny's favorite and dearly loved friend.

Fanny loved to visit Phoebe in her home on Bedford Avenue. This was a home where Presidents, Union Generals and everyone who was anyone dined. Their $30,000 organ was built in and was often used to entertain the finest guests. Fanny loved to play it.

Phoebe's father was the Methodist Evangelist, Dr. Walter C. Palmer, and husband, Joseph, was one of the founders of the Metropolitan Life Insurance Company. The couple was very wealthy.

It was not a secret that Fanny was paid on the average of $2.00 per song by the Bigelow and Main Company and Phoebe did not approve. She had no trouble expressing to Bigelow & Main or others that she felt Fanny was underpaid and overworked! It was well known that Phoebe was unhappy with Bigelow and Main but Fanny never complained.

Fanny told Phoebe she did her work for the Lord and thanked Bigelow and Main for allowing her forty years of blessings, peace and tranquility, "...like the dew on the mountains of Zion."

Phoebe felt Fanny gave much to the world and she should have the finest things. She wanted to help financially but Fanny could see no need in abundance. Whenever Fanny had extra money she gave it away. Eventually, Phoebe began to take Fanny to the store and buy her things or have clothing made instead of giving her money.

Every year the two would meet and stay for a week at the Savoy Hotel downtown New York. There they would shop, dine and talk into the wee hours of the morn like school girls. In the summer of 1908 Fanny did not know it would be their last time. Just a few days later, on the tenth of July, Phoebe Knapp died of a stroke while on vacation in Poland Springs, Maine.

Greenwood Cemetery — Grave of Phoebe Knapp
Brooklyn, New York

Rev. Dr. Robert Lowry

Fanny met Dr. Lowry in 1866 when he composed the music for her hymn *All the Way my Saviour Leads Me* I will try to relate this story to you.

Fanny and two other hymn writers worked in Dr. Lowry's office for a time. He would read to them selections from favorite authors during the long summer afternoons and she remembered his reading Browning's, Rabbi Ben Ezra, a poem of which he was fond and how it reminded them of the good doctor.

"Grow old along with me, the best is yet to be, the last of life for which the first was planned," he would read.

As a critic Dr. Lowry was possessed of excellent taste and they never so much as thought of appealing any decision of his whenever the question in dispute related either to poetry or music. Fanny said his ear was trained to detect the most minute metrical fault. In 1897 he assisted Fanny in the selection of her best hymns and poems for a book called **Bells at Evening** for which he wrote a biographical introduction.

Fanny said, "Ere long, however, Dr. Lowry's health began to fail and we watched him with growing anxiety." She would always recall their last meeting at his home in Plainfield, New Jersey, with tender emotions. They talked together about the events of thirty years and, finally, he said, "Fanny, I am going to join those who have gone before, for my work is now done."

She could not speak with him concerning the parting without betraying her grief so she simply took his hand in hers and said quietly, "I thank you, Doctor Lowry, for all that you have done for me. Good night, until we meet in the morning." Then she silently went down the stairs, knowing that the good man would soon be at rest from his labors, and so indeed it proved.

A little while to weep for those we cherish,
As one by one they near the river's brink;
A little while to catch their sweet assurance,
That we in heaven shall find each missing link;
A little while and then the glorious dawning
Of that fair morn beyond the swelling tide,
When we shall wake and in our Saviour's likeness,
Perfect and pure, we shall be satisfied.

"Although some of my most treasured friends have passed beyond the sound of human voices, others remain to add their graceful benediction to a life full of blessings and already crowned with peace." Fanny said.

William Howard Doane

William Howard Doane

William Howard Doane was born in Connecticut in 1832 but lived and ran his business in Cincinnati, Ohio. Mr. Doane took over his father's cotton goods store when he was sixteen and became successful. His second career was that of hymn writing.

In the year 1867, Fanny met Mr. William H. Doane under interesting circumstances. He came from his home in Cincinnati to New York to visit his friend, Dr. Van Meter of the Five Points Mission, and they were looking for a hymn to use for the Mission's anniversary.

Several hymns were given to Mr. Doane but he did not find them appropriate.

About this time Fanny was writing More Like Jesus and Dr. Lowry asked Fanny why she did not send it to Mr. Doane.

She said, "Well, I will," and on November 5,1867 sent it by a messenger boy. This is the way the story went as told by Fanny.

The lad handed Fanny's words to Mr. Doane, who happened to be at the moment talking with Dr. Van Meter and he laid them down for a few minutes. When he took up the letter and glanced over its contents he started after the boy but could not find him. He returned to Dr. Van Meter disheartened, but determined to find

Fanny if she were in the city. He hunted for her the rest of the day and, about eight or nine in the evening, he was finally directed to her boarding place. She went to the door.

He asked, "Are you Fanny Crosby?"

On being told she was that person he said, "Oh, how glad I am to find you; I have been trying to do so a long while and at last I have succeeded."

At the close of their interview he said, "I must pay you for the hymn that you sent." He put into her hand what she supposed to be a two-dollar bill and then bade her good night. It turned out to be twenty dollars, more than she ever received before.

One evening Mr. Doane took Fanny's hymn More Like Jesus to Dr. Van Meter. Mr. Doane said, "I have something else; and if we can find an organ I will play it for you." They went into a neighboring church and Dr. Van Meter agreed to pump the organ while Mr. Doane played and sang the hymn. Soon Dr. Van Meter burst into tears and forgot to pump the organ. They tried again, and this time Dr. Van Meter came out from behind the organ, threw his arms around Mr. Doane's neck and cried "Doane, where did you get that?"

Then Mr. Doane told him that Fanny Crosby sent him the words and he had just written the music. The hymn was used at the anniversary and was a great success.

Dwight Lyman Moody

Dwight Lyman Moody

"I have never known a kinder, bigger-hearted man than Dwight L. Moody." Fanny said.

From the memories of their meeting Fanny wrote:

> My own recollections of Northfield bring back many incidents concerning those whom it was my fortune to meet there. So strong was the friendship existing between Mr. Moody and Mr. Sankey that we used to call them "David and Jonathan" and I am sure that the modern church has not known two men more devoted to the work of Christian evangelism. And so they went far and near, telling the old, old story in sermon and in gospel song until the influence of their meetings spread through all classes of society.

Fanny's last personal message from Mr. Moody was received shortly before his death while she was conducting a series of meetings in Oneonta, New York. A friend of Fanny's carried a message of greeting to Mr. Moody to which he exclaimed, "Oh, Fanny Crosby, give her my love."

Little did Fanny know this would be her last message from Dwight Moody. Several months later he would "sleep on the summit of old Round Top," where they gathered many beautiful summer evenings to hear his words of comfort and of inspiration.

Fanny would say, "Dwight Lyman Moody was a wonderful man; the following passage from the Holy Book was always in her mind as she would think of his blameless life:

> Blessed are the dead which die in the Lord from henceforth.
> Yea, saith the Spirit, that they may rest from their labors, and their works do follow them."...Revelation 14:13"

Dwight Moody is buried at Northfield, Mass.

Ira D. Sankey

Ira D. Sankey

Fanny met Ira D. Sankey in 1876 for whom she said she wrote some of her most anointed songs.

Of her dear friend, Ira Sankey, Fanny said, "It is a blessed joy that Mr. Sankey, for twenty-five years has been a close associate of mine in writing gospel hymns. His work as a composer and as a singer is known throughout the length and breadth of the Christian world. For the sorrowing and unfortunate of both America and Great Britain he has done an amount of good that eternity alone will be able to estimate and his own sweet melodies have indeed been a balm to many an aching heart. The friendship of this talented man is one of my priceless jewels. During a recent illness I told him that I believed the entire Christian world was praying for his recovery."

He said, "Tell those who love me and are praying for me that I am holding on to Christ and Christ is holding on to me; and that by and by I'll see Him face to face and tell the story, *Saved by Grace* (One of Fanny's well-known hymns) when I shall wake within the palace of the King."

During the summer of 1894 Mr. Moody was holding a series of evangelistic services. One evening Mr. Sankey came to Fanny and said, the audience has requested that you speak.

She felt that she was not prepared she said, "Oh, Mr. Sankey, I cannot speak before such an array of talent."

Dr. Pierson supplemented Mr. Sankey's request by saying, "Yes, you can. There is no one here of whom you need be afraid."

Then another man said, "Fanny, do you speak to please man or to please God?"

"Why, I hope to please God," she replied.

"Well, then," he said, "go out and do your duty."

During her remarks that evening she recited for the first time in public the words to *Saved by Grace.*

"Where have you kept that piece?" asked Mr. Sankey, when she returned to her seat.

She told him that she kept it stored away for an emergency. There was a reporter present that evening. He wrote down the hymn and a few weeks later it appeared in an English religious paper. At Mr. Sankey's request, Fanny's friend, George C. Stebbins, composed the music to *Saved by Grace* and thus the hymn was sent forth on its mission to the world.

The following is a note written to Fanny from Ira Sankey,

> Dear Fanny, co-laborer in the blessed service of sacred song for so many years:
>
> I wish that when you get to heaven (as you may before I will) that you will watch for me at the pearly gate at the eastern side of the city; and when I get there I'll take you by the hand and lead you along the golden street, up to the throne of God, and there we'll stand before the Lamb, and say to Him: And now we see Thee face to face, saved by Thy matchless, boundless grace, and we are satisfied.
>
> Yours till the day dawn and the shadows flee away,
> Ira D. Sankey

One day while Fanny was visiting with Ira he gave her this note,

"I wish you to convey to all my friends, the assurance of my love; and that I hope to meet them all by-and-by in the land where there is no more sorrow nor pain, and where God shall wipe away all tears from our eyes. Tell them that God is Love and that I have ordered those words to be cut on my tombstone in Greenwood, that future generations may know the faith in which I died. .

Yours, till the day dawn and the shadows flee away,
Ira D. Sankey.

Fanny said, "Years ago, when the weather was nice I used to travel and visit with Mr. Sankey. He was suffering from an illness causing him to lose his sight. When I visited I would make him get up to play the piano and sing. I encouraged Mr. Sankey that his sight will return someday when he will see the face of Jesus."

Fanny was an important friend to Mr. Sankey as he suffered with blindness caused by glaucoma during his later years. Their friendship was so strong that Mr. Sankey paid for Fanny's and Carrie's living expenses in Bridgeport.

In an interview at his death Fanny recalled their last meeting, "We wept and prayed and sang together. Later he wrote to me asking me if I got to Heaven before him to watch for him at the Pearly Gate at the Eastern side of the City."

"When I get there, I will take you by the hand and lead you through the Golden Street to the Throne of God, and there we will stand before the Lamb and say to Him: *And we are satisfied, and now we see Thee face to face, Saved by Thy matchless boundless grace, and we are satisfied.*

"It has been told many times that as Mr. Sankey slipped into a coma, he was singing the words; *Someday the silver cords will break, and I will no more as now shall sing, but, oh, the joy..."*

Ira Sankey died on August 14th, 1908 he was 86 years of age. The funeral services were conducted in Theodore Cuyler's church. Dr. Charles E. Locke of Brooklyn preached the sermon. At the conclusion of the sermon the church quartet sang *The Ninety and Nine, There'll Be No Dark Valley,* and *Sleep On, Beloved.*

Fanny Crosby and Ira D. Sankey

Ira D. Sankey's grave maker.

Ira Sankey is buried at Greenwood Cemetery in Brooklyn, NY. Section 125 Lot #30550.

Philip Bliss

The death of Philip Bliss at the beginning of what seemed a career of great promise cast a cloud over all of his friends. He died in a terrible railroad accident at Ashtabula, Ohio, while trying unsuccessfully to save his beloved wife.

The night before, he said to his audience, "I may not pass this way again." Then he sang a solo, *I'm Going Home Tomorrow.* This indeed proved prophetic.

This is the story as told to Fanny by Ira Sankey. Ira had been waiting at the hotel for Mr. Bliss to arrive in Chicago for a revival they would do together.

> "I was seated at a small cabinet organ in a hotel in Chicago that sad Saturday morning, awaiting the coming of my friends. The hour of their arrival had passed, and someone remarked, that the train must be late. Then a friend rushed into the room and, laying his hand on my shoulder as I was singing one of Bliss's hymns, said, Sankey, Bliss is dead! All were shocked and for a time could not believe the story but in a few minutes others brought confirmation..."

Fanny and Ira would miss their dear friends greatly but would continue to remember one of his hymns, *Wonderful Words of Life.*

Philip was introduced to Fanny on June 4th, 1864. Fanny always loved the story of when he was just ten years of age and heard a piano for the first time. Becoming so taken by the sound he went searching to see what it was. He found it coming from the parlor of a stranger. He did not think, entered and there found a young lady seated at the piano. She immediately ordered him out. Philip then determined that he would learn music. Mostly through his own efforts, he became so proficient in music that, after a few years, he was teaching and directing large choirs.

Mr. William J. Kirkpatrick

Fanny met William.J. Kirkpatrick while at Ocean Grove Camp Meetings in Ocean Grove, New Jersey. He was a skillful professor. Fanny visited him at his home in Philadelphia several times and she looked back upon these occasions with pleasure.

To some of the melodies that he sent she wrote words that have been used for many years in gospel services. A few of the titles are *He Hideth My Soul, He Came to Save Me, Redeemed, Welcome for Me and Meet Me There.*

George C. Stebbins

Mr. George C. Stebbins wrote the music to *Saved by Grace, Eye Hath Not Seen, Come Unto Me, Ye Weary* and *In Perfect Peace.*

Too Many to Tell

There are many other musical people that Fanny had the honor of knowing. She numbers them among her dearest friends. The list includes Hart P. Danks, William F. Sherwin, Dr. Horatio R. Palmer, Samuel Alman, T.F. Seward, C.G.Allen, Bentley DeForest, Silas Vail, A.M. Wortman and countless others.

Fanny's Mission

It was morning. We were on the porch, Fanny and myself, alone. Eva left to run errands. Flo and Jule had gone to the market.

"Aunt Fanny, I know that your occupation was that of a hymn writer, but we all have something that is dear to us. You know, our own personal passion? What is the passion of your own ministry?"

"Hurting people!" Fanny said. "Alcoholics, prostitutes, down and out people. I loved them all."

I settled back in my chair as Fanny shared these stories.

"Some of the most gratifying memories of my life center about testimonies of those whom I have been able to help by words of cheer.

"Shortly after my arrival at Ocean Grove, New Jersey in 1877 I was met by a man whom I had known in the old Norfolk Street Church in New York. Twelve months before I had seen him under totally different circumstances. Then he was disheartened, now he was thrilled with Christian hope and we were indeed surprised by the complete transformation. On the evening of our previous meeting he arose and said, 'Friends, I know I have done wrong; and

Fanny Crosby speaking to a large group of men.
Fanny is far left, middle of picture.

many times I have asked your prayers. But tonight I must have your help.' His manner impressed me exceedingly and I gave him some words of cheer but the majority of our members had little faith in his affirmation, because he had tried so many times and failed. His greeting to me at Ocean Grove was as follows: 'I want to thank you for your kind words in my behalf at the Norfolk Street Church.'

"The work of the Christian missionary has always had a fascination for me that all other callings have lacked. It was a rare privilege to sit at the feet of the saintly Bishop William Taylor and hear him tell of the tribes which live where "Africa's sunny fountains pour down their golden sand," as Bishop Heber has said in his great missionary hymn. The good Bishop Taylor bore the heat of the day until his locks were snowy and his strength ebbing fast.

"On one occasion when he was starting for Africa he said to me, 'Fanny, if you were thirty years younger would you go with me to Africa?' 'Yes indeed, I would,' I answered, 'and help you plant missions.'

"I saw him again a few weeks before his last missionary journey and he said, 'Well, Fanny, I am going once more.'

'Many times yet,' said I, 'if it be our Father's will.'

"Laying his hand upon my head he gave me his blessing and, as he stood there, a vision of the multitudes of whom his ministry had been a benediction came before my eyes with a strange power and pathos. My prayer is: May the hour come when we will no longer say of the foreign field, 'Lo, the harvest is ripe, but where are the reapers?'

"The unique illustrations given by Dr. Talmage always interested me, one of them in particular.

"In a Christmas sermon he told the story of a little Swiss girl who was dying, and from her window she could look out to the lofty summit of the mountains amid which she had been reared. 'Papa, carry me to the top of the mountain,' she exclaimed. He replied, 'My child, I cannot carry you, but the angels will.' For a time she was silent and lay with her eyes closed. At length she opened them and looking out of the window exclaimed in her joy, 'They are carrying me, father. I shall soon be at the top.'

"With those words Dr. Talmage concluded his sermon. It seemed to his hearers that he conducted them to a high pinnacle in a lofty range of mountains where they might breathe a pure atmosphere. When I reminded him of the beautiful effect that his words had upon us, he said, 'Ah, you are right. I never intended to bring you down from that summit.'

"And thus it is with even the humblest fellow-ministers of song; they take us to heights of which the soul often dreams, yet rarely attains, in fact to those mansions of the blest where there are always light and warmth and love; where the thirst of weary pilgrims is quenched by draughts of mountain springs; and where this mortal spirit puts on its immortality."

Sing on, ye joyful pilgrims,
The way will not be long
My faith is heavenward rising
With every tuneful song.

The Y. M. C. A.

The rapid growth of the Young Men's Christian Association gratifies my heart and I am glad to know that railway officials and other employers are coming to realize more and more that it is to their mutual advantage to encourage this noble work. In witness of the growing sentiment in favor of the Y. M. C. A. I need but refer to the increasing number of buildings that are erected yearly for the accommodation of young men of all classes, and for their intellectual and moral improvement.

"Richard C. Morse was known to me as early as 1868; and one morning—I think it was in 1871—he came to my home before breakfast, and asked, 'What are you going to do today?' I replied that I had no particular plans and was entirely at his service. He then told me the sad story of a poor drunkard who attempted to commit suicide. Mr. Morse had taken the man to his own room and given him something to eat and, as he appeared to be more comfortable, had now come to me to see what we together could do for his conversion. The man was finally redeemed and afterwards became a minister of the gospel. That was my first work among men."

In 1880 Fanny conducted frequent services for the railroad branches of the Christian Association.

She told, "As I was entering a surface car one afternoon I chanced to step on the conductor's foot; and I cried, '0, conductor, I know that I have hurt you, but I did not intend to. Will you please forgive me?' He replied, 'You didn't hurt me at all; and if you had you made up for it by speaking a kind word.' I believe it was his remark that turned my attention toward the work among railroad men. Before the month passed I was invited to the home of my friend William Rock, who was superintendent of a surface car line in New York. He was in the habit of gathering a few Christian men together on each Sabbath morning to hold a prayer service for the railway employees. Only a few came at first but finally the little room in the car station was filled with railroad boys. Although this was not a permanent organization, Mr. Rock's little company formed one of the first associations of railroad men in active Christian work.

"The following year I met with members of the Rail-road Branch of the Y. M. C. A. which had recently been organized at Hoboken. The quartet of men was Tom Keenan, Jerry George, James Berwick and Benjamin Locke. A week after their meeting they invited me to visit the association at Hoboken. There I met Mr. J.L. B. Sunderlin, then secretary in that city, and from that date at least twice each year we held a pleasant reunion.

"Since 1882 I have addressed the men of the Christian Association in various towns and cities and they have given me such a warm place in their affections that I have been obliged to adopt five or six hundred of them throughout the Eastern States. They, however, in turn have adopted me and the Hoboken Branch some years ago gave me a beautiful little badge of honorary membership.

"I am glad to be able to quote a stanza from a Christmas poem written for the Railroad Branch of the Young Men's Christian Association about 1901:

How I would like to shake your hands,
And greet you one by one;
But we are now too far apart,
And this cannot be done.
Yet I can hope, and wish, and pray
That Heaven's eternal joys
May fall like dew upon your heads,
My noble railroad boys,"

The Bowery

Fanny's connection with the Bowery Mission dates from 1881. Mr. Childs was its superintendent. Fanny first knew him as a discouraged man out of work but always found him a true Christian gentleman. He had given up an excellent position in Massachusetts because of failing eyesight and came to New York to find something to do. They first met on a street car and Fanny asked him if he was familiar with the Bowery Mission. He said that he was. The next evening they went down there together and she introduced him to the Rev. Rulifson, the superintendent. He immediately began leading men to Christ.

Fanny told, "I frequently attended the evening meetings at the mission and one evening they asked me to speak. During my remarks I said, 'If there is a man present, who has gone just as far as he can go, he is the person with whom I want to shake hands."

Mr. Childs whispered, "The man for whom you are looking sits directly in front of the platform."

"When the meeting closed I was introduced to this stranger and asked him if he did not wish to come out and live a Christian life?"

"Oh," he replied, "what's the difference? I have no friends; nobody cares for me."

" 'You are mistaken,' I said, 'for the Lord Jesus cares for you; and others care for you too. Unless I had a deep interest in your soul's welfare I certainly would not be here talking with you on this subject.' Then I gave him several passages of Scripture and he seemed moved to consider the matter carefully.

"At last he said, 'If I come here to the meeting tomorrow evening and sign the pledge, will you come with me?'

"To which question I replied, 'Yes, I will be here again; and, although I do not discourage you from signing the pledge, it seems to me that the best pledge you can give is to yield yourself to God. Will you do it?'

"The next evening he was present; before the close of the meeting we saw the new light in his eyes and felt the change in his voice."

"Fanny," I said. "I am touched by your burning desire for these people. I now understand where your line, *Touched by a loving heart, wakened by kindness*, from your hymn, *Rescue the Perishing,* comes from. Kindness in this world will do much to help others, not only to come into the light, but to grow in grace day by day."

Fanny stated, "There are many timid souls whom we jostle morning and evening as we pass them by but if only a kind word was spoken they might become fully persuaded. For all mission workers everywhere I always have tender sympathies. God bless them!

"Many of my hymns have been written after experiences at the New York missions. One in particular has been used far and wide in evangelistic work.

"As I was addressing a large company of working men one hot August evening, the thought kept forcing itself upon my mind that some mother's boy must be rescued that very night or perhaps not at all. So I requested that, if there was any boy present who wandered away from his mother's teaching, would he come to the platform at the conclusion of the service. A young man of eighteen came forward and said, 'Did you mean me? I have promised my mother to meet her in heaven; but as I am now living that will be impossible.' We prayed for him; he finally arose with a new light in his eyes; and exclaimed triumphantly, 'Now, I can meet mother in heaven; for I have found her God.'

"That evening the line came to me, *Rescue the perishing, care for the dying,* I could think of nothing else. When I arrived at my home I went to work on it at once. I rocked in the quiet and put together the words. This hymn would not be for the lost; it was for all the Christians who miss the chance of reaching out to the lost. For the Christians who refuse to give their time. For the men and women who are either afraid or ashamed to mention the name of Jesus in public. Those who should be sharing the Gospel of Jesus Christ to all, no matter who they are or what they've done!

"Before I retired the entire hymn was ready for a melody. The next day my words were written and forwarded to Mr. Doane, who wrote the beautiful and touching music as it now stands.

Rescue the perishing, Care for the dying,
Snatch them in pity from sin and the grave;
Weep o'er the erring one, Lift up the fallen,
Tell them of Jesus the mighty to save.

Rescue the perishing, Care for the dying;
Jesus is merciful, Jesus will save.

Down in the human heart, Crushed by the tempter,
Feelings lie buried that Grace can restore;
Touched by a loving heart, Wakened by kindness,
Cords that are broken will vibrate once more.

Rescue the perishing, Duty demands it,
Strength for Thy labor the Lord will provide;
Back to the narrow way, Patiently win them,
Tell the poor wanderer a Savior has died

Rescue the perishing, Care for the dying;
Jesus is merciful, Jesus will save.

"In November 1903, I went to Lynn, Massachusetts, to speak before the Y. M. C. A. I told them the incident that led me to write *Rescue the Perishing*. After the meeting a large number of men shook hands with me and among them was a man who seemed to be deeply moved.

" 'Miss Crosby, I was the boy, who told you more than thirty-five years ago that I wandered from my mother's God. The evening that you spoke at the mission I sought and found peace and I have tried to live a consistent Christian life ever since. I have preached the gospel for over 35 years. If we never meet again on earth, we will meet up yonder.'

"As he said this, he raised my hand to his lips and before I recovered from my surprise he had gone. He remains to this day a nameless friend who touched a deep chord of sympathy in my heart. It is these notes of sympathy that vibrate when a voice calls them forth from the dim memories of the past, and the music is celestial.

Touched by a loving heart, wakened by kindness,
Cords that were broken will vibrate once more.

"One evening, at a meeting, there was a man in the seat in front of me. From his singing I judged that he was under conviction. Something within prompted me to ask him if he would remain and hear the sermon, and he finally consented to do so. Just before the close of the address I whispered, 'When the invitation is given, will you go to the altar?'

"For a moment he hesitated, and then asked, 'Will you go with me?' I did go to the altar with him and had the pleasure of seeing him a saved man.

"I could give more than one instance where men have been reclaimed after a long struggle and many attempts at reformation because someone spoke a kind word to them even at what appeared to be the last moment. I have also known many others who turned away from a meeting simply because the cheering word had not been spoken nor the helping hand extended. Never to chide the erring has always been my policy for I firmly believe that harsh words only serve to harden hearts that might otherwise be softened into repentance.'

Speak not harshly when reproving
Those from duty's path who stray;
If you would reclaim the erring,
Kindness must each action sway.
Speak not harshly to the wayward,
Win their confidence, their love;
They will feel how pure the motive
That has led them to reprove.

The anniversaries at the Bowery Mission were always notable occasions and those who had been converted there made a special effort to be present, many of them coming from long distances. Fanny was present and made a short address at sixteen of these gatherings; and on each occasion also wrote a hymn. Victor H. Fenke, for so many years their organist, was one of Fanny's friends and he composed the music to a number of her hymns.

"Jerry McAuley, for many years, was one of the most widely known men in New York. It was in his own mission on Water Street where I first met him. The story of his life, how he had been a thief, a drunkard and a thoroughly desperate man deeply interested me because of the work of grace wrought at his conversion. As a speaker he used simple language but his manner was so impressive that all men were drawn toward him. He and his faithful wife toiled, planned and sacrificed to give the old Water Street Mission a start. Not long after my first visit with them they were instrumental in founding the Cremorne Mission on West Thirty-second Street; and there I was introduced to Mrs. E. M. Whittemore, the founder of the Door of Hope for unprotected girls.

"I knew both of the Hadley brothers, they were such mighty forces for good in the missions of New York. Col. Henry Hadley I met many years before his conversion, which occurred at the Jerry McAuley Mission. When I first knew him he was a skeptic and was in many ways hostile to the Christian cause although he was always kind to everyone. At that time he was a successful lawyer and the editor of a prominent New York paper.

"One evening there was a knock at the door about nine o'clock, and someone asking, 'Is Miss Crosby up?' I knew his voice and was convinced that he had come to tell me of the glad news of his conversion.

"I have something to tell her,' he said, 'I have found the Lord.' During the seventeen years of his Christian life he founded sixty missions.

"Besides often making speeches for various organizations such as the Young Men's Christian Associations, Sabbath schools and churches of many denominations; during the years of 1885-1900 I was led to write some of my most abiding hymns: *Jesus is Calling, My Saviour First of All, Blessed Day, Resting by the River, Never Say Good Bye, He Hideth My Soul, Meet Me There, Come with Rejoicing, Safe in the Glory Land, and Yes, There is Pardon for You."*

Eva took a chair. "My this has been a serious day!"

"A lot of history," Fanny said. "I am surprised at the number of names and dates I can easily recall."

"Aunt Fanny, I do believe that we have some letters to answer and then we shall be on our way for the day. You need to rest."

"Will you be back in the morning?"

"You are really enjoying yourself aren't you, Fanny?" Eva asked.

"Most definitely. Maybe I can tell about some funny times tomorrow."

"Sounds good to me." I said.

"Then that settles it! We will be back in the morning." Eva ended our conversation.

I wasn't sure about Fanny but I was exhausted. That afternoon I took the time to lie on the bed for just a few minutes and found myself waking the next morning.

Funny Times

Eva and I arrived a little later than normal. We ran errands on the way.

There on the porch waiting for us were Flo, Henry, Jule and Jule's daughter Mrs. Leschon. Lined up in their rocking chairs along the porch—a sight to behold!

"Good morning Aunt Fanny," Eva and I said at exactly the same time.

"Good morning," she responded.

"Looks like we aroused some curiosity this morning." I said.

"Wouldn't miss this for anything." Henry answered. "Would you ladies care for something to drink before you start?"

"No thank you."

Eva said, "Yes, I would like something thank you. I believe I breathed in some dust from the street this morning."

I began by asking Fanny what was the earliest funny memory she could clearly remember. She thought for a moment and then began.

"While living in North Salem mother and I would attend the Quaker Meeting House near Peach Pond. We remained there for five years among the Quaker families and I learned many things, including the plain language. One day a friend of mother's was going to the mill and I wanted to go along.

"He said: 'No, thee ain't going with me.'

"I replied: 'David, I tell thee I am going to the mill with thee.'

"To which he answered: 'Well, get thy bonnet and come along.'"

"While living in Ridgefield I was playing tag on the Village Green with the other children. They were amazed at the way I could play; my hearing was sharp and they could not hide from me. While playing I ran into a tree and about knocked myself out. As the other children left laughing, one of my friends, Sylvester (Vet) Main, helped me up and walked me home. On our way I told Vet how embarrassed I was. I just couldn't understand running into that tree. The shade of the trees usually warned me when I was close. Vet explained there were no leaves on that tree, it had been dead for years. I questioned as to why the founding fathers would leave a dead tree on the village green. Thirty years later I of course would meet Sylvester Main again in the office of William Bradbury. He was one of the owners of Bigelow and Main Publishing Firm."

"Between the ages of eight and fifteen my poetry would begin to make the newspapers. One of my first published poems ended up in the newspaper without my knowledge. It was printed in the "Herald of Freedom" a small weekly newspaper published by P.T. Barnum at Danbury, Connecticut. There was a miller near Ridgefield who was dishonest in many of his dealings and of him I wrote, not expecting it to be made public:

There is a miller in our town,
How dreadful is his case;
I fear unless he does repent
He'll meet with sad disgrace."

"The teachers of the Institution liked to read to their students from famous poets. This of course, did not disappoint me. Some of the teachers at the institution were strict and would not allow any talk between the boys and girls. I was one of the first to revolt. We knew that one of the faculty of the Institution was taking some notice of one of the lady teachers and, to even accounts with them, I wrote the following lines:

Say, dearest, wilt thou roam with me
To Scotland's bonny bowers,
Where purest fountains gently glide,
And bloom the sweetest flowers.

Ah, Martha, may we soon retire
Unto some pleasant cot,
Where love and joy forever dwell
And sorrow is forgot.

There in the gentle summer eve
We'll watch the murmuring streams;
The moon shall fondly cheer our hearts
With it's majestic beams.

Then, let the wintry blasts appear,
And all the flowers decay;
We'll sit beside the cheerful fire,
And sing dull care away.

"Not many months after my verses were written the unpopular teacher and his Martha did as I suggested, and they left the Institution."

"During the winter months in Ridgefield a music teacher would come into town twice a week to give singing lessons. I really enjoyed this. One evening we were practicing the famous *Handel and Hadyn*. When the rest of the singers stopped singing I was left singing alone. I was frightened by the sound of my own voice and I began to cry. The teacher spoke kind words to me and assured me that I had not committed any offense.

"I can still hear some of the sweet voices of my friends reverberating through the old Presbyterian meeting-house; the tuning fork of the choirmaster as he 'set' the pitch; and the rich mellow tenor of the minister as he answered the choir from the pulpit.

"During the long winter nights I loved having people read to me. My favorites were the romantic tales of the Wild West and the stories of Robin Hood and his remarkable brigands. My most favorite story was *Rhinaldo Rhinaldine, the Bandit.*

"Not many months passed ere my mind was teeming with the accounts of charitable bandits whose habits in general were to rescue the poor wayfarers and send them on their journey with money in their purses. For the sake of variety a few bad robbers were sometimes thrown in but sooner or later their chief would always emerge when they least expected it. He would compel them to return their dishonest gains and the end of the story was not reached until they repented of their mode of life and actually reformed. In some cases, though, a term in prison was necessary to settle them in their new purpose."

"Aunt Fanny," I said, "Do you suppose this was the start of your great love for the homeless, the prisoners?"

Everyone erupted in laughter.

Then Jule said, "You may be right. I had never thought of it that way. Fanny has always been interested in the less fortunate. Mother said even as a child Fanny would cling to those who were desperate or to the orphaned animals."

"I guess that I have never looked at it that way Jule," said Fanny. "It may have been the beginning. I love to find the down and out and lead them to the Lord; to see them repent of their mode of life. You may have a very good point, Darlene."

"One of my dearest friends at the school was Alice Holmes, a fellow poet. Alice was a deep thinker and a genius at mathematics. I well remember the day she came to us from her home in Jersey City. We were apprised of her coming and determined to give her as good a reception as we could lest she should become homesick, as many of us had. Since she was to occupy a portion of my room it devolved upon me to make her feel at home and very soon we were conversing about all sorts of things. I found that she was a

Fanny Crosby and Alice Holmes

member of the Episcopal Church, while I was an adherent of the Methodist, and the contrast between us in this respect suggested a bit of doggerel. Walking demurely toward her couch in the farther end of the room, just as she was about to retire, I said, 'Alice, I have a piece of poetry, which I would like you to hear; and will you please tell me how it sounds?'

Oh, how it grieves my poor old bones,
To sleep so near to Alice Holmes,
I will inform good Mr. Jones,
I can't sleep with a churchman."

"Alice Holmes and I went on to be life long friends."

"On one occasion in 1850 a lady came to visit the school. She said, 'There is one place I would like so much to see.' 'What is that,' I asked, for I had already shown her most of the school.' 'Why I am very anxious to see your children eat; how do they find the way to their mouths?' 'Oh, well,' I replied, 'If that is all, you shall see. We take a string, tie one end of it to the table leg; the other end to our tongue and then we take the food in our left hand, and feel up the string with our right until we come to our mouth.'"

"On another occasion the superintendent of the school told me there was a gentleman in the waiting room, would I please show him around the institution? I was only too glad to do so; and as we walked through the school the stranger picked up a copy of my book, ***The Blind Girl and Other Poems***. Not knowing it was me he said, 'Oh, here are Miss Crosby's books. You know her well, I suppose?' 'I am aquatinted with such a person,' I said, deciding to have a little fun. 'Is she not very amiable?' he asked. 'Oh no, far from it,' was my reply. 'Well I am sorry to hear that,' he said, 'But I will take one of her books; and will you please tell her?' As he was leaving, he handed me his card, and I learned that the visitor was the celebrated Professor Tellcamp of Columbia College. The incident immediately brought to my mind the scriptural advice, *Be* *not forgetful to entertain strangers, for thereby some have entertained angels unawares.* I was never to see Professor Tellcamp again."

"Oh, how embarrassing!" I said.

"It most certainly was!" Fanny replied.

"In the fall of 1844, as a preliminary to publishing a volume of poems, they told me I must have my daguerreotype (picture) taken for the frontispiece (foreword). In those days no less than four minutes were required for an exposure and the idea that I, the restless Fanny Crosby, as they all knew me, would be obliged to sit still so long—well, that was indeed funny. As a result I burst into a laugh right in the midst of my "sitting" and, of course, spoiled a plate for the photographer. Then the tedious process began again; a veritable inquisition it was for me but finally I endured to the length of five whole minutes and secured a fine picture."

"Sometimes two or three of my associates would accompany me when I went home for the summer vacation and mother liked them to come as often as possible for she loved the society of young people. A humorous incident happened during one of these visits that is good enough to relate here. Among my friends came a young man who wore a wig. Mother did not know it; and one evening, when there were several present, he complained of a severe cold in his head. '0h, I think I can cure that,' said my mother. He replied, 'Never mind; I'll get over it.' But she was evidently bent upon working a cure; and despite the remonstrance of the young man, proceeded to rub some salt on his scalp, whereupon the company knew the fact of the wig. The young man was considerably embarrassed; and mother of course heartily wished she had let him alone."

"Once when General Scott came to visit the institution, he was examining a collection of maps that were used by our pupils, one of the aldermen present,—for they always came to our receptions,—stepped to my side and whispered, 'The General's sword is just a little out of place.' 'Let us remove it quietly,' said I.

"With his aid I carefully drew it out of the great sheath without attracting attention and then suddenly held it above the head of the intrepid warrior. 'General Scott,' I exclaimed in an authoritative tone, 'you are my prisoner.' Although taken completely by surprise, he was by no means at a loss for an answer. 'Oh, I surrender; I always surrender at discretion to the ladies.' He laughed good-naturedly, as did those who saw the incident; and we turned the subject. A moment later, however, he said, 'Well, Miss Crosby, the next time I come here I suppose some young man will have run off with you.'

"Forgetting that he was a candidate for the presidency, I exclaimed, 'Oh, no, I shall wait for the next president.' This announcement on my part was followed by a tremendous roar of laughter, and I found myself in an uncomfortable position."

"During my early life I was connected with the Democratic Party and one afternoon during the summer I was sitting in the parlor singing bits of Democratic songs. Before I knew it, two gentlemen came into the room, one of whom walked toward me with the request that I favor them with another song.

"When I finished singing, he said, 'Then Mr. Clay is not your candidate.' 'No,' I replied, 'but I have a profound respect and reverence for him, and also for Mr. Frelinghuyson,—yet they are not my candidates.' At that moment Mr.Chamberlain came up and presented me to the two strangers. To my utter consternation I found that one of them was Mr. Frelinghuyson himself. 'Mr. Frelinghuyson,' I said, 'you have heard me express my views already; and for me to say that I did not mean it would be telling a falsehood. But I would not have said what I did, had I known you were present, —so please take it for what it is worth.' He laughed heartily and replied, 'I give you credit for your candor.'

"I would later change to the Whig party and then to the Republican Party where I have remained."

"In general I have been always willing to agree with authors as to the merits of their own poems. That often is the safer plan, and in the end may save a vast deal of ill feeling. One funny instance comes to mind now. Fifty or more years ago I knew a man who thought he had a genius for poetry; and when I was calling at his house he recited one of his own productions, of which I recall only this stanza:

"I am what is called a sinner
By those who think they are right,
But then I hope to go where
The blind receive their sight."

"I said, 'Why, Mr. Brown, did you write that?' Endeavoring to look as demure as possible. He seemed to be much flattered and said, 'I have been thinking that you and I could write a book together.' Summoning all the gravity I could, I exclaimed, 'Wouldn't that be splendid!' The book, however, was never written."

"Certain rumors have been circulated among some who do not know me to the effect that my health is fast declining. About fifteen years ago there was a gentleman in New York, who, hearing that I was dead, took the occasion to preach a funeral sermon; another time my publishers received a telegram, while I was dictating a hymn that I had just written, asking at what hour Fanny Crosby passed away; and at still another time a New York paper published that my death was momentarily expected, —but none of these things moved me. Nor do I believe any of the recent reports as to the declining state of my health, where they originated I do not care. To the good Lord be the praise that they are not true; and I patiently await the time when He Himself shall come to write my obituary in the Book of Life. Until then I hope to continue to labor with all the energy that I can command."

This poem Fanny wrote about an actual incident with Mr. Chamberlain, the Superintendent of the Institution;

THE PRESUMPTUOUS MOUSE

Dear friends, receive attentively
A strange account of Mr. C.
With your permission I'll relate,
Though you may smile at his sad fate,

How while reposing on his bed,
And airy thoughts flit through his head,
A weary mouse house-hunting crept,
Close to the pillow where he slept;

But there not feeling quite at ease,
And wishing much himself to please,
He looked with grave and thoughtful air
in Mr. C's disheveled hair.

"Ah, here's the station I like best,"
Said he, "and here I'll build my nest.
This scalp conceals a poet's brain,
So here till morning I'll remain,

Perhaps the muse will me inspire,
And if she tune her magic lyre,
I'll to the world proclaim that we,
That mice, like men, may poets be?

Our hero thus descanted long
On love, and poesy and song;
While now and then a gentle squeal
His vocal powers would reveal.

His strain of eloquence it broke,
For Mr. C, perplexed awoke,
And starting up - "I do declare
There's something scraping in my hair;

A light; a light; what shall I do?"
At this the mouse, alarmed, withdrew;
And had he not, I'm certain, death
Had stopped, ere long, his little breath.

"I need a break," Flo said, "we all need a break."

"Let's go in and look at some more pictures," Fanny said. "Eva, can you bring out the photo albums?"

"I will." Eva said.

Flo took me on a tour of 226 Wells Street, explaining the pictures on the walls. There were pictures of Mercy, Fanny, Carrie and Jule. All over the house were mementos of Fanny's life.

Fanny sat down at the piano and began to play at which point everyone began to sing.

Fanny said, "Open the windows and let the music rise to heaven!"

I sat across the room trying to absorb all of the memories I could. I never want to forget this moment, I thought.

Later, I found myself sitting alone in the parlor with Fanny.

"What are you thinking about, Darlene?" Fanny asked, "I can feel curiosity."

"I was wondering how you handle people who seek you for advice on teaching the blind, writing poems, as well as those who merely are interested in your life? How do you answer their spiritual questions?"

"My advice is this, I am not bothered by theology, doctrine, church membership or denominations. My advice is simply, does it come from God? Does it line up with the scriptures? My ultimate authority is always, the Bible. My advice is always, do you have a relationship with God?"

"Tell me Aunt Fanny do you believe in Satan, in evil?"

"I do believe that evil exists, I do believe in Satan, but I also believe that God can take the evil in this world and use it for good. I have often quoted this scripture: Hebrews 12:6 *Whom the Lord loveth, He chasteneth,* I have often said, if I had no troubles, I would think that the Lord did not love me. Take that Doctor who caused my blindness so many years ago. I know that Satan meant that to destroy me but I have never once felt pity for myself or blamed the doctor. Bless his soul, he is probably dead by now but if I could talk with him, I would tell him that he did me the greatest favor in the world. I have not been distracted by worldly goods and the lack of sight was replaced by a vision in my soul."

"I know that you plan to live to be 100 years old. That means you have six more years, at least. What is your desire for the rest of your life?"

"If I live to be 100 only the good Lord knows. I do rest in the thought that when I cross to the other side I will receive my sight and the first thing I will see is my Saviour's face; and like my song I shall know Him.

When my life's work has ended, and I cross the swelling tide,
When the bright and glorious morning I shall see;
I shall know my Redeemer when I reach the other side.
And His smile will be the first to welcome me.

I shall know Him, I shall know Him,
And redeemed by His side I shall stand;
I shall know Him, I shall know Him
By the print of the nails in His hand.

"I have been asked if I am retired, I always answer that I have yet to write my best hymn. In 1910 my health began to fail. I am nearly bent in two by old age. It is hard for me to get around, slowing me down a bit but not stopping me. I want to live to be one hundred and five. Unless the Lord thinks otherwise.

"October of 1912 I was stricken with pneumonia. Everyone held their breath, they thought this would be the end of Fanny Crosby. To their surprise I recovered and continued to travel.

"In February 1913, Flo and I traveled to Cambridge, Massachusetts to speak at the First Baptist Church. One evening I spoke to an audience of 2000."

"My ninety-third birthday fell on Easter day and I was heard to say, "Is there anyone happier than I, I want to shake his hand, for I believe myself to be as happy as it is possible for a mortal to be in this world. Life with me glides on like a little boat on a waveless stream, with flowers on each bank. That evening I spoke at the

First Methodist Church and George Stebbin was there, he had come from Brooklyn to help me celebrate.

"My ninety-fourth birthday was proclaimed as Violet Day. Nationwide the Methodists wore Violets in honor of Fanny Crosby's birthday. I spoke at the First Methodist Church once again, everyone thought this time it would be my last speech. The newspapers reported this way:

> Fanny Crosby was feeble in body, yet strong in mind, buoyant in spirit, with a trust and faith in God as firm as the everlasting hills. She spoke about the power of prayer, she said; "I do not kneel to pray anymore, I no longer have the strength to rise from that position. I want all of you to go to God in prayer in all trials and sorrows. Good will come out of it, and He will answer your prayer better than you think. Of course, one may not always get exactly what is requested. But one must trust God's way is best. Cling to the Saviour, in this age of change. My dear, dear people, I love you dearly, and when I should cross to the beautiful shore, I know that I shall greet you there! I believe that He still has work for me yet."

"Aunt Fanny, what is your formula such a good long life?"

"A diet of eggs, fruit, vegetables, chicken and tea; keeping one's temper; speaking no evil; creating a poem from 10 to midnight and repeating it to a copyist in the morning; and carrying a little book."

"I pray daily for my country. I don't like the way I see things going. The Bible must be the center of every home and we must be served by a President who prays. In the newspapers I try to follow the ministries of Billy Sunday and other evangelists. I pray that they will take the place of Moody and Sankey."

"In an article written about me the writer said,

> Passing now through the later seventies of her useful life, she preserves all the sprightliness of her early years. Her friendships are fervent, and her hope is strong. She loves her work, and she finds her rest in Christ. In her younger days she joined the Methodist Episcopal Church, and its fellowship is still her comfort and delight. She engages in no doctrinal controversies, but speaks the language of Zion with saints of every name. She sits in her easy chair, holding an open book before her closed eyes, working her

> vivid concepts into hymnic phrases which her amanuensis writes down. Thus she spends her days, waiting her appointed time. When it comes, she will open her eyes on the glory that shall be revealed, and take her part in the new song."

"Wasn't that pretty?"

"It certainly was and this has been a wonderful day. You have known a lot of famous and interesting people."

"Important people also," Fanny added. "We have talked a great deal about me but I have heard nothing about you. What do you do for the Lord Darlene?"

"I sing your hymns along with many others."

"You are a singer?"

"Yes."

"Wonderful, let me hear you sing."

Maybe tomorrow. I must find Eva now and let you rest. Can we talk again tomorrow?"

"Will I hear you sing?"

"Yes."

"Then we may."

Of Presidents and Famous Friends

We were greeted with a flurry when Eva and I arrived.

Flo said, "You may only talk a little while this morning, we are attending the Jesse Lee Celebration picnic today over in Easton."

"Fanny, if you would rather we can skip our talk this morning."

"On the contrary dear, here, have a seat, we must get started before Flo makes me start getting ready. Oh, remember, you promised to sing for me today."

"Yes, I remember and I will. Fanny can you tell me how you came to know all of the Presidents in your lifetime. The list that you knew is quiet impressive. Do you have any favorite personal stories about any of them?"

"The presidents that I personally knew were;

John Quincy Adams 1825-1829
Andrew Jackson 1829-1837
Martin Van Buren 1837-1841
William Henry Harrison 1841
John Tyler 1841-1845
James Knox Polk 1845-1849
Zachary Taylor 1849-1850

Millard Fillmore 1850-1853
Franklin Pierce 1853-1857
James Buchanan 1857-1861
Abraham Lincoln 1861-1865
Andrew Jackson 1865-1869
Ulysses Simpson Grant 1869-1877
Rutherford Birchard Hayes 1877-1881
James Abram Garfield 1881
Chester Alan Arthur 1881-1885
Grover Cleveland 1885-1889
Benjamin Harrison 1889-1893
Grover Cleveland 1893-1897
William McKinley 1897-1901
Theodore Roosevelt 1901-1909
William Howard Taft 1909-1913
Woodrow Wilson 1913-1921"

President John Quincy Adams

"In April, 1847, a delegation from the institution again appeared before Congress, with students from Boston and Philadelphia institutions. During our stay in Washington we had the privilege of hearing the last speech of John Quincy Adams. The audience was so still that the faintest noise in any part of the room seemed to be loud, and we waited breathlessly to hear what the aged statesman would say to the rising generation. His voice had lost much of its original sweetness but power fell upon our ears with a strange cadence that echoed in my memory for many years after the voice itself ceased to be a great and commanding force in the councils of our nation.

"John Quincy Adams died of a brain hemorrhage in February of 1848. I composed an elegy entitled, *Weep Not for the Dead."*

President Martin Van Buren

"While I was still in school I had dinner one night with then former President Martin Van Buren. He was impressed with my intelligence and I considered him a man of fashion and elegance. He was in his sixties but I had a schoolgirl crush on him."

President William Henry Harrison

"In the autumn of 1840, General William Henry Harrison was elected President. Everyone loved the hero of Tippecanoe; the opposing parties tried hard to find something to use against him but could not. He lived for only one month after being elected. Of his death I wrote;

He is gone: in death's cold arms he sleeps.
Our President, our hero brave,
While fair Columbia o'er him weeps,
And chants a requiem at his grave;
Her sanguine hopes are blighted now,
And weeds of sorrow veil her brow.

Ah, Indiana, where is he,
Who once their sons to battle led?
The red man quailed beneath his eye,
And from his camp disheartened fled.
With steady hand he bent the bow
And laid the warlike savage low.

The forest with his praises rung,
His fame was echoed far and wide,—
With loud hurrah his name was sung,
Columbia's hero and her pride.
The tuneful harp is now unstrung
And on the drooping willow hung."

President John Tyler

"In the summer of 1841 President John Tyler came to visit the school and I was called upon to welcome him with a poem. It's ending was:

> And this the glad song of our Nation shall be,
> Hurrah for John Tyler and liberty's tree."

President James Knox Polk

"While the students of the Institution were in Washington, in 1847, James Knox Polk was president. President Polk invited us to the White House and, during the course of the conversation, he said, 'Well, Miss Crosby, have you made any poetry since I saw you last year?' 'Yes sir,' I promptly replied, 'I have composed a song and dedicated it to you.' 'My announcement was as much of a surprise to my friends as to Mr. Polk, himself, for I kept it a secret; but he appeared to be much gratified and asked me to take his arm and proceed to the music room where we held an impromptu recital.

"During this appearance before Congress they requested me to recite a poem and I gladly consented. Some of my friends maintained that I was the only woman who appeared before the joint session of the Senate and House of Representatives.

"1848 was an important year, not only for the country at large but for the Institution also. The nation was entering upon a new era of prosperity after the Mexican war and all eyes were turning toward the South to face the grim prospect of another dreadful conflict. This time, however, within our own borders, a struggle was going on that was to decide once and for all a number of the great questions in dispute. Already there was some talk of disunion but all anxiously hoped that the government might find some way out of the difficulty. The discussion of important national affairs was interesting to the pupils. During this time, while the school was interested in public affairs, it was exciting for us to receive visits from three statesmen, all of whom were taking a prominent part in the government of our nation. One of these men was President of the United States and the other two wanted to be. They were James K. Polk, Henry Clay and Winfield Scott.

"After serving a number of years in Congress, Mr. Polk had been elected governor of Tennessee and, in 1844, he was nominated against Clay and won the election. The following summer Mr. Polk returned the school's call, coming unexpectedly and unattended. He was a very plain man and did not wish any ceremony at his reception. He said that he had simply come to their beautiful retreat to escape the turmoil of the busy city.

"After dinner I asked President Polk if he would enjoy a stroll through our grounds. Everything that day was in the height of its beauty, the trees formed a double arch over the walks in our yard; in the lofty boughs many robins and bluebirds built their nests and entertained us with their sweet carols. The soft winds came stealing through the leafy boughs, laden with perfume from the flowers of a score of nearby gardens.

"We had not gone many yards before I heard the familiar voice of an old domestic to whom I was indebted for many favors. The dear old woman was not at that time in the employ of the Institution, but had just returned for a few minutes to speak with some of us and I knew that I might not see her again for months. This thought was uppermost in my mind, at that moment; and so I turned impulsively to President Polk and said, 'Will you please excuse me a minute?' 'Certainly,' he replied; and so I left the chief man of the nation standing alone while I ran to greet my friend.

"Realizing my discourtesy on my return, I made all manner of apologies and tried to explain the circumstance as best I might. To my surprise, however, the great and good man said, 'You have done well, and I commend you for it. Kindness, even to those in the humblest capacity of life, should be our rule of conduct; and by this act you have won not only my respect but also my esteem.'

"I hitherto held a high opinion of President Polk but from that moment his kind words elevated him to my own ideal of a Christian gentleman; and that night, ere I sought my pillow, I fervently prayed that God would bless and sustain our worthy president in the arduous duty of executing the laws for more than twenty millions of people.

"My interest in public affairs has never abated. There are not many people living in this year of grace who had the privilege of meeting such statesmen as Henry Clay, General Scott, and President Polk but the names of these heroes are recorded with indelible letters among the annals of our national history and their imperishable deeds are chronicled in characters that no person living should wish to efface. They were men of sterling worth and firm integrity, of whom the rising generation may well learn wisdom and the true principles of national honor and democracy that all of them labored so faithfully to inculcate. And that the men of this present age and of generations to come will continue to remember the dignity and honor that the past has bequeathed to our own and future times, no loyal American need have one iota of doubt."

President Abraham Lincoln

"I was shocked and suffered with disbelief when informed that my favorite President had been murdered. To me, Abraham Lincoln towered over all the other Presidents. He was, indeed, my captain and leader. To have known him seems to have brought me in close touch with all that is great in history."

President Grover Cleveland

"President Grover Cleveland, I knew the best. One morning in 1853 William Cleveland, one of my co-Teachers, had a favor to ask of me. His brother had been hired as the secretary to the superintendent of the school. William asked me to speak with his brother and help him over the loss of his father.

"That afternoon I went into the office and found Grover Cleveland, a young man of about seventeen, engaged in his work as private secretary. We exchanged a few sentences and I agreed to come again the next day; from the hour that we first met a friendship sprang up between us, the links of which must have been woven by angels fingers.' During the hours when he was not working, he would write my poems as I dictated them.

"Many years later when a daughter was born to the Clevelands, I wrote:

Like the lily bells that blossom
In the bowers of Eden fair,
All their pretty leaves unfolding
To the breeze that murmurs there,

Like a jewel bright Dan sparkling
From the peerless brow of Truth,
Like a birdling with the autumn,
Came your winsome Baby Ruth.

There are feelings deep and tender,
There are joys you could not know
Till a cherub in your household
Bade the hidden fountains flow.

Now, above its smile reflecting
From the peaceful eye of Truth,
Like a radiant star is shining
O'er your gentle Baby Ruth.

In a fancied dream I linger,
As the evening time draws nigh,
And I listen to the carol
Of her momma's lullaby,

While her papa, grave and thoughtful,
As in years of vanished youth,
Lays his head with fond caressing
On the head of Baby Ruth.

By a holy consecration
That will ne'er forgotten be,
You have answered him who whispered
'Bring your little ones to me.'

You have brought her pure and lovely,
To the Way, the Life, the Truth,
And His seal is on the forehead
Of your precious Baby Ruth.

May you train her in the knowledge
And the wisdom of the Lord,
May you teach her to be faithful,
And obedient to His word.

With the lamp, whose beams are kindled
At the throne of sacred truth,
May you guide the coming future
Of your darling Baby Ruth."

"Aunt Fanny I understand that this is the Baby Ruth the candy bar was named after!"

"At my eighty-fifth birthday party a letter from President Cleveland was read:

> My dear friend,
>
> It is more than fifty years ago that our acquaintance and friendship began; and ever since that time I have watched your continuous and interested labor in uplifting humanity, and pointing out the way to an appreciation of God's goodness and mercy.
>
> Though these labors have, I know, brought you abundant rewards in your consciousness of good accomplished, those who have known of your works and sympathized with your noble purposes owe it to themselves that you are apprised of their remembrance of these things. I am, therefore, exceedingly gratified to learn that your eighty-fifth birthday is to be celebrated with a demonstration of this remembrance.
>
> As one proud to call you an old friend, I desire to be early in congratulating you on your long life of usefulness, and wishing you in the years yet to be added to you, the peace and comfort born of the love of God.
>
> Yours sincerely, Grover Cleveland

"These letters from my friend I prize among my most valued treasures; and of all the great men in public life whom I have known, I consider him to be one of the greatest; and in my affection and esteem he holds a place that no other statesman could possibly occupy.

Upon learning of President Cleveland's death Fanny said in a newspaper interview on June 25,1908:

> "He left an impression that will never be effaced—
> that of a noble, faithful Christian gentleman,
> and with that impression there was that deep,
> warm friendship that death cannot break,
> for the cords will be united and we shall see and
> know each other in the land of the blest."

Of Grover Cleveland's funeral the newspaper reporter wrote;

> When our great Union General was laid to rest on Riverside Drive, Gilmore's great band of five-hundred pieces played Miss Crosby's hymn, "Safe in the arms of Jesus," as the body was lowered into the vault. I stood with that immense throng that afternoon in the woods that faced the Hudson. I shall never forget the solemn hush that spread over that huge gathering as the last note of Fanny Crosby's beautiful hymn died in the gathering dusk, and we realized that our Great Warrior was at last at peace.

Other Distinguished Gentlemen

Henry Clay

I regretted not being able to see Henry Clay in the Senate, but in the following spring, in March of 1848, he made a tour of the large cities and, as a specially invited guest, came to the Institution. About thirteen months before this time, his son and namesake had fallen while fighting at the battle of Buena Vista and I had written a poem, in memory of Colonel Clay, which Mr. Chamberlain sent to his father. The great statesman was never himself after his son's death and I purposely avoided all mention of it in the address of welcome on the day he came to visit, lest I might wound the heart of the man.

"There was a strength in his character and an earnestness in his speeches that appealed to me more than I can tell. I used to liken Clay to Richard Henry Lee, and Webster to Patrick Henry; for one was as gentle as the murmur of a rippling stream, the other rushed onward with the strength of a mountain torrent, sweeping all before him by the force of his mighty intellect. I thought Clay the more winning of the two; and I would have challenged any person, whether Whig or Democrat, Northerner or Southerner, to come within range of that man's eloquence without being moved to admiration and profound respect; for his personal magnetism was wonderful.

"Mr. Clay came to the Institution at about ten o'clock in the morning and we were prepared to welcome him in princely style. The band greeted him with Hail to the Chief; and then we opened our ranks and allowed him to pass between two files of musicians to the chapel upstairs where the rest of us were assembled. Mr. Chamberlain gave some eloquent words of greeting and I gave my poem of welcome. When I finished reciting it, Mr. Clay stepped forward and, drawing my arm in his own, led me slowly to the front of the platform. 'This is not the only poem,' said he, 'for which I am indebted to this lady. Six months ago she sent me some lines on the death of my dear son.' His voice trembled; while both of us stood there weeping. Finally he controlled his emotion and delivered one of the most eloquent addresses to which I have ever listened. He had a deep rich voice that echoed with strange sweetness throughout our chapel as it rose and fell with feeling and we were charmed by his eloquence. Not many months after his visit to New York, Mr. Clay was again elected to the United States Senate, and the old fire seemed to return to him when he arose to debate some important measure, or to propose some great compromise, like the "Omnibus Bill" which bore his own name. Still his health was impaired, and soon afterward he slept with his fathers at Ashland, Kentucky.

Sleep on, oh statesman, sleep,
Within thy hallowed tomb,
Where pearly streamlets glide,
And summer roses bloom."

General Winfield Scott

"In the early spring of 1848 General Winfield Scott made a triumphal entry into New York which was almost as notable as that other entry into the city of the Montezumas. The events of the Mexican war were still fresh in our minds, and we were eager to meet the hero who had won the name of 'Old-Rough-and-Ready.'

He came, however, a little before we were prepared for him; I was sent for, to entertain him until the time set for the afternoon exercises. From such an honor I shrank at first, but the great general had not spoken half a dozen sentences before I was at ease; his quiet and kindly manner was so reassuring.

"'General Scott,' I said, 'when you found yourself really within the halls of the Montezuma, did you not feel like shouting ?'

"'No,' replied the soldier, 'we felt like falling down here on our knees to thank the good Lord for our victory.' Later in the afternoon he said, 'No, we did not revel in the halls of the Montezuma; we lived on one meal a day.'

"General Scott, being the candidate of the Whigs at the election of 1852, was defeated by one of his subordinate generals in the Mexican war, Franklin Pierce, of whose political party I was an adherent. Consequently, after the election I wrote a little song entitled, *Carry Me On,* most of which has been forgotten, except the chorus, which goes as follows:

O Whigs, carry me on, carry me far away,
For election's past and I'm pierced at last:
The locoes gave gained the day."

Count Henri Gratien Bertrand

"On one occasion the school was visited by Count Henri Gratien Bertrand, Field Marshal for Napoleon. I was to write a poem of welcome for him and part of it is as follows:

When by those he loved deserted,
Thine was still a faithful heart;
Thou wert proud to share the exile
Of the hapless Bonaparte.

Like an angel, whispering comfort,
Still in sickness thou wert nigh;
And when life's last scenes were over
Tears of anguish dimmed thine eye.

"When I finished reciting the poem, the Count exclaimed, 'Oh, how did you know that I sat with my head in my hands and wept as the life of the great general slowly ebbed away?'

"I did not know, but described the circumstance from imagination. He gave me a box containing a piece of willow that grew above Napoleon's grave as he said, 'God bless you, how I wish you could have known the emperor.'

"I always admired the courage of Napoleon, though I could not love him as a man; and so the devotion of his faithful Marshall touched my heart."

Flo interrupted, "Aunt Fanny, do you need to rest before the picnic today?"

"No!" Fanny answered sharply.

Flo looked quizzically at her and walked away. Fanny seemed to be impatient today, she seemed to be on a mission to finish her story. In a few minutes Flo returned with a tray of lemonade and some cookies.

"Here's a snack for the two of you as you continue your talk." she said.

Fanny's First Appearance Before Congress

"During the summer of 1843 I was ill. A party from the school was going to Washington to appear before Congress. I had not yet fully recovered. Dr. Clements said that I would fret myself into a serious sickness if they left me at home; besides the trip South might do me some good. It was finally decided by the Board of Managers that Dr. Clements would go and take care of me; yet, when I learned that I was expected to deliver a poem before a joint session of both houses of Congress, my heart sank within me.

"I would not have agreed to the arrangement, were it not for the fact that our parties were trying to impress the legislators of the absolute need of schools for the blind in every state of the Union. Any chance of doing a little for them I would not let pass; and so there I was a timid mortal not in the best of health, to deliver an address before the most distinguished body I have ever seen.

"I tried to do my best; and when I finished my poem there was a dreadful silence which I interpreted to mean the audience was not pleased. I stood with mingled emotions, alternating between hope and fear. Then there was such a tremendous applause that I was actually frightened. I was asked speak more and repeated some lines that had been written and published the summer before in memory of the Hon. Hugh S. Legare, The lamented Secretary of State, who died suddenly while going with President Tyler to attend the exercises at the laying of the cornerstone of the Bunker Hill monument. I will quote three stanzas of my tribute:

Farewell, esteemed departed one, farewell,
Deep solemn tones have pealed thy funeral knell,
Thou to the grave art gone. Sweet be thy rest!
For angels guard the relics of the blest.

Hark, hark, thy requiem floats upon the ear, So deeply sad.
We pause; we weep to hear.
Ye patriot Sons of fair Columbia's shore,
A brilliant star has set, to shine no more.

Weep, oh, Columbia, o'er his lonely grave,
Then let the cypress, sorrow's emblem, wave,
The mournful breezes sigh, wild flowerets bloom,
And breathe their fragrance o'er his hallowed tomb.

"My lines of tribute evidently took the senators by surprise and I was told that many of them wept. The occasion was sad for me, because the sister of Secretary Legaré was in the audience, having come all the way from Georgia to see our pupils, and to meet the writer of the poem for she had already seen it in the papers. When I came out of the Senate chamber she met me at the door and placed a beautiful ring on my finger. The following year she came to New York to visit us and I had the pleasure of presenting her with the first copy of ***The Blind Girl and Other Poems.***

"Not only did I know distinguished men in the government but I knew Indian dignitaries as well. Chief Albert Cusick of the Onondaga Indians was a favorite friend."

Fanny and The Onondaga Indians

Each summer for seven years I made a delightful pilgrimage to the beautiful Finger Lakes region of New York and to the Chautauqua Assembly on the shores of Tully Lake. Here I have found, close to Nature's heart, one of the best things that earth has to offer any mortal and that is the immortal friend of kindred spirits. There I delivered annually a poem before the Chautauqua Round Table.

"Next to good bandits I had been deeply interested in the Indians; and you may be sure that I was highly delighted, as well as honored, when Albert Cusick, formerly chief of the Six Nations, now chief of the Eel Clan and my personal friend, told me that he would adopt me into the Eel Clan of the Onondagas. The rite of adoption was performed in the summer of 1904 but you need have no fear of me, for the hatchet has been buried these many years. Being now an Indian myself, I was afforded the right to tell Indian legends."

"Aunt Fanny how did you travel to New York?"

"I boarded the train in Bridgeport and traveled to Tully. Once there I was met and taken by carriage to Tully Lake. It was always a delightful trip."

CHAUTAUQUA GREETING written by Fanny J. Crosby
(Dedicated to the Round Table, August 10,1906)

In these classic wilds of beauty,
In our summer land so dear,
Crowned with blessings rich and boundless
We have gathered year by year.

From the village and the hamlet,
From the city's crowded streets,
In our summer home so tranquil,
We are spared again to meet.

Hail, Chautauquan sons and daughters,
Swell the chorus; let it break
O'er the forest and the mountain,
O'er the waves of Tully Lake.

Like Minerva, rich in wisdom,
Dropping words like gentle dew,
Still our President is with us,
And her magic wand we view.

While our noble, kind director,
Warmly as in years before,
Gives to each a cordial welcome
To Assembly Park once more.

Silver lake and giant forest
Many hours like this recall,
While they sing with tuneful measure:
Happy greetings one and all!

Are we all at our Round Table?
All who gathered years ago?
No, some tender links are broken,
And our tears awhile must flow.

Far beyond the silent river,
Some have laid their burdens down;
They have heard the Savior's welcome,
And received their promised crown.

Now they bid us weep no longer,
But enjoy the pleasant hours,
Till by angels we are wafted
To their paradise of flowers.

Hail, Chautauquan sons and daughters,
Nature joins our song of love;
Happy greeting, happy greeting
To our temple in the grove.

Reflecting on Life as a Blind Person

"Fanny if you could tell the world about being blind or encourage the blind what would you say?"

"This gift of seeing is one that ought to inspire in the heart of him who possesses it many tender emotions of gratitude to the Eternal One, who, amid the splendors that encircled His throne, lifted a mighty voice, and through the chaotic gloom that held in midnight darkness the silent deep, uttered the sublime command, *Let there be light.*

"It has always been my favorite theory that the blind can accomplish nearly everything that may be done by those who can see. Do not think that those who are deprived of physical vision are shut out from the best that the earth has to offer. There are a few exceptions that instantly come to my mind. For example, through the medium of sight alone, does the astronomer mark the courses, the magnitudes and the various motions of all the heavenly bodies; and only through the medium of the eye can the sculptor produce a beautiful statue from the rude and uncut marble. His sight must guide him in reproducing the image that is already modeled in his own mind; and so likewise of the painter, he frequently pauses in his busy hours and turns to gaze toward the rich crimson clouds which fall so gracefully amid the glories of the autumnal sunset. He must try to reproduce the vision that he gets from them, and it is only through the eye that the picture of the actual cloud enters.

"From attaining high ranks in these fine arts the blind of necessity, are debarred; but not so from poetry and music, in which the mind gives us a true image of the reality.

"Almost every lad at school was able to relate stray bits of legendary lore of ancient and modern artists who have been blind. Indeed, who can forget Euclid, the blind geometrical; or Homer, the blind bard; or Milton, the author of that beautiful apostrophe to light.

"A great many people fancy that the blind learn music only by ear, never by note; and yet a number of musical experts have told me that their blind students learn as proficiently as others by the latter method. It is truly wonderful, marvelous—to what a degree the memory can be trained, not only by those who rely upon it for most of their knowledge of the external world but by all who wish to add to their general intellectual culture.

"But why should the blind be regarded as objects of pity? Darkness may indeed throw a shadow over the outer vision; but there is no cloud, however dark, that can keep the sunlight of hope from the trustful soul.

"One of the earliest resolves that I formed in my young and joyous heart was to leave all care of yesterday and believe that the morrow would bring forth its own peculiar joy; and, behold, when the morrow dawned, I generally found that the human spirit can take on the rosy tints of the reddening east. Early and late I played with children of my own age; and our elders were in the habit of remarking that Fanny Crosby was certain to be interested in any mischief that could occur. With the agility of a squirrel I used to climb trees and ride horses as fleet as the wind while I hung on to their manes for dear life; and climb stone fences, in every respect, just like other children. Whenever I tore my dress I managed to keep out of my mothers sight until I fancied she would not notice it, which was a rare occurrence indeed."

"As a young girl I was taught to knit and crochet."

"How?" I asked.

Fanny said, "Let me show you something, Eva! Eva..."

"Yes, Aunt Fanny?" Eva answered.

"Will you bring a few of my doilies out here and show them to Darlene?" Fanny asked.

Within minutes Eva came through the door carrying a couple of beautifully crocheted doilies! "How did you do that?" I was astounded!

Fanny laughed. "It is simple, I learn how to make the stitch and then I count." Fanny replied.

Flo joined us. "I believe it is time to leave for the Jesse Lee Memorial picnic. You are most welcome, Darlene, to go along."

"How nice of you Flo," Fanny said. "My niece is one of the most thoughtful people I know."

Henry gathered up things to put in the basket, Flo and Mrs. Leschon carried quilts and off we went. Flo, Henry, Eva, Mrs. Leschon, myself and of course Aunt Fanny.

Jesse Lee Memorial Picnic, Easton, Connecticut
1914

The Picnic

Soon the quilts were spread out and the basket was opened. Henry and Flo had prepared the food the evening before. There was fried chicken, hard boiled eggs, biscuits and, of course, watermelon. It was wonderful.

While eating Henry told a story of Fanny's mischief while still a girl. The Institution decided to grow watermelons one year to raise money. Fanny awoke in the middle of the night and persuaded some of the other girls to join her in raiding the patch. By morning they had eaten most of the watermelons and all were known to have a stomach-ache for the next several days.

Fanny shook her head and mumbled that some things would best be left untold.

After the picnic people visited, games were played, everyone attending the picnic gathered for a picture and now everyone was relaxing.

Fanny took me by the hand.

"Let's go for a walk, just you and I."

I looked toward Eva, she nodded.

I placed Fanny's hand around my arm as I had seen Henry do many times and off we went.

"Fanny, how do you write such anointed hymns?"

"I believe that God gives them to me." she said.

"Every one of them?"

"Yes!"

"Does He talk to you, do you actually hear Him? How does He speak to you?"

She began to talk and talk and talk. Telling me of things I was seeing. As if showing me them for the first time. How did she know what I was seeing?

"You see that large oak tree? It must be close to one hundred years old. And look at the lake and the flowers around it! The lilies, the daffodils, tulips and roses? Look at the colors, yellow, red, pink, white."

I turned to look. There were all the colors she was talking about. But how? How did she know? I had to know! "How do you see them?" I asked.

"Look at the flowers. Are they not the most beautiful things you have ever seen?" asked Fanny.

That was it! I stopped! I took both of her hands as I pulled her facing me. "How do you know?" I said. "How can you see them?"

"I have seen them through different eyes. I have seen through others' eyes and I have felt with my hands and smelled their fragrance. I have seen them with my mind. I have seen the flowers in this park many times. Come let me show you."

Pulling me toward the water she said, "Lead me to the roses,"

I led her to the roses.

She said, "Now close your eyes and feel them! Tell me what you feel."

"I feel roses."

"No!" she said getting impatient with me, 'tell me what you REALLY feel?"

"I feel soft, velvety petals."

"How many?"

"Lots"

"How do you know they are roses?"

"I have felt them before."

"Feel the stem. Remember how they feel. Now smell, what do you smell?"

"I smell roses."

"How do you know?"

"I have smelled them before."

"Take me to the petunias, close your eyes and feel them. What do you feel?"

"A single soft petal, narrow, like a tube at the bottom opening to a wide top, kind of frilly at the top."

"See how they differ from the roses? Feel their stems'. Remember that feel."

"The stem is smooth," I said.

"Smell them. Do they smell different?"

"Yes, a very sweet smell."

"Remember their smell. Now, listen. What do you hear."

"I hear a whippoorwill."

"How do you know it is a whippoorwill?"

"I have heard one before!"

"Wait! Stop! Keep your eyes closed! Do you smell that? Right now, smell. What is it?"

"I smell... lilacs."

"Do you have your eyes open?"

"No."

"How do you know it is lilacs?"

"I can tell by the smell. I remember what they smell like."

"My dear, that is what it is like with God. Once you have been with Him you never forget. You know what He feels like, what He sounds like and what He smells like. He fills up your senses. The next time He tells you something you know it is Him."

"Oh, Fanny, you make it sound so easy."

She continued, "The more time you spend with Him the easier it becomes to know Him. A week ago you and I did not know each other, now we do. You come to know God by spending time with Him!"

I asked Fanny, "Do you think that you have missed anything by not being able to see?"

Good!

"See what? God is the most important thing in my life. Have you seen Him? Because of my blindness, I have seen more than most sighted people will ever see."

"You certainly have. I want to thank you for sharing this with me and the time you have spent with me this week. It means more than you will ever know."

"We're not finished yet, there is plenty of time. Before you leave today, I want to show you my mother's grave. We will ask Henry to drive us there. I intend to be buried there but not until I have seen 100 years, unless the Lord says otherwise. We must be getting back. Flo and Eva will be getting anxious."

I placed Fanny's hand around my arm and off we went to join the rest.

Henry came down the path to meet us. "Fanny, they are ready for the picture now and if we are going to stop by the cemetery before dark we must be going." Henry said.

"That is why we were headed in your direction."

Henry took Fanny's hand and helped her into the buggy. Then helped me, Eva, Flo and finally climbed in himself.

"Well Henry," Fanny said, "how does it feel to be escorting four ladies at one time?"

"I believe I like it, Aunt Fanny!" Henry answered and off we went.

It had been a lovely warm August day, now the sun was setting and a cool breeze was beginning to blow.

Soon we were turning between the gates into the cemetery. Henry took me on a tour as Fanny told what I was seeing.

"Mother's grave is over to the right but on your left is my friend, P.T.Barnum. The founder of the great Barnum Circus. He passed not long ago. They have placed a large lovely monument on top of him."

Henry stopped the carriage and came around to help us out. As we walked across the grass Fanny told of the relatives buried around Mercy. Showing me where Carrie was buried. She stopped and dropped on her knees. I ran quickly and knelt beside her thinking she had fallen.

She said, "And this...this is where I will be laid to rest. But you can be sure that only the clay will be in the ground for I will be *Safe in the Arms of Jesus*. I love that song. As long as others sing my hymns I will continue to live. Sing this with me Darlene, I do want to hear you sing." She took both my hands into hers and held them tight as if she would never let go. We began to sing,

Safe In the Arms of Jesus,
Safe on His gentle breast,
There by His love o'er-shaded,
Sweetly my soul shall rest.

Hark tis the voice of angels,
Born in a song for me,
Over the fields of glory,
Over the jasper sea,

Safe in the arms of Jesus,
Safe on His gentle breast.
There by His love o'er-shaded,
Sweetly my soul shall rest.

"Are you alright? Dar, are you alright?"

I turned to see who was speaking to me, it was Dennis.

I blinked! I shook my head! I tried to clear my eyes! I sat down for a minute and looked around. I was back in...1996.

Dennis continued talking, "I was wandering around when it dawned on me it was getting late. I came to find you and saw you fall on your knees. Did you slip and fall? Are you alright? What were you singing? We'd better be going before we get locked in the cemetery for the night."

I turned to look, hoping not to see...but it was there, Fanny's grave. I felt the tears welling inside. "Oh, I've lost her!" I said.

"Who?" Dennis asked.

"Fanny, I'll never let go"... "Fanny, she's gone."

"She's not gone, she's right here!" said Dennis

"No, that's just her grave," I said.

"Honey, are you okay?" Dennis kept asking me questions. My head was swimming.

"I think I'm alright?" But was I? Was I losing my mind? I had just experienced one of the most fantastic...most fantastic what? Was it a dream? Was it real. It seemed so real. I sat back down. I said, "Dennis, please sit down, I have something to tell you!"

The Diary

The next morning I was still a bit confused but determined. We went to the Bridgeport library. In the archives was the historical folder of Fanny Crosby. I frantically thumbed through the pages...where is it, I thought! Please let it be here. Oh, please...she promised me...finally! There it was! Pages from Eva's diary. She wrote;

> "In August, 1914, Aunt Fanny suffered a heart attack. When she recovered she spoke of a glorious vision seen during her illness. Fanny throughout her life spoke of visions and dreams. This time an angel had come to her and said; "Be thou faithful, and I will give thee the crown of life. Be calm and get your strength back as soon as you can, and then go back to work for the Master once more. When telling of this vision she said, "When I have arrived in my eternal home, they will say, 'Come in, Fanny! Come in!' Then will be the victory through Christ."
>
> In the next few months she wrote a dozen hymns including Keep Thou Me.
>
> She began to make her funeral arrangements and made Florance and Jule promise not to place a monument of granite or marble on her tomb but instead to have a home for needy people, as a living monument to her.
>
> February 9, 1915 Rev. Henry A. Davenport, of the People's Presbyterian Church, visited with Fanny and remarked that Fanny

was glowing and he was not the first to speak of this. Others said it was if she were glowing ever since her last vision.

February the tenth she greeted visitors and even played a duet on the piano with one of them.

February eleventh she didn't feel well and stayed in bed most of the day. She called for me about nine o'clock PM and dictated a poem for a neighbor family who just lost their daughter, reassuring them that their little ones was "*Safe in the Arms of Jesus.*" After the letter Fanny dictated to me her last poem:

"In the morn of Zion's glory,
When the clouds have rolled away,
And my hope has dropped its anchor
In the vale of perfect day,
When with all the pure and holy
I shall strike my harp anew,
With a power no arm can sever,
Love will hold me fast and true."

At 3:30AM, February 12th, 1915, with Florance by her side, Fanny was *Safe in the Arms of Jesus.* The doctor arrived at 4:30AM to pronounce her dead of a cerebral hemorrhage.

Aunt Fanny was honored with one of the largest funerals ever held in Bridgeport, Connecticut. People stood in line for blocks to file by the coffin. Pastor Davenport prayed at great length. Dr. George M. Brown said, "You have come to pay tribute and to crown a friend. There must have been a royal welcome when this queen of sacred song burst the bonds of death and passed into the glories of heaven.

The honorary pallbearers were: Ira Sankey's son, Allen; Sylvester Main's son, Hubert Main, composer; George Stebbin and family friend, S. Trevana Jackson. Children not one tenth Fanny's age sang her hymns. The choir sang Fanny's favorite hymn, *Faith of our Fathers* then they sang some hymns written by Fanny, *Safe in the Arms of Jesus* and *Saved by Grace* as many wept openly.

Everyone at the funeral was given a violet, as they passed by the coffin they placed their violet inside her casket, they said it seemed as if she were sleeping in a bed of violets.

When my life's work has ended, and I cross the swelling tide,
When the bright and glorious morning I shall see; I shall know
my Redeemer when I reach the other side.
And His smile will be the first to welcome me.
I shall know Him, I shall know Him,
And redeemed by His side I shall stand;
I shall know Him, I shall know Him
By the print of the nails in His hand.

I continued to search through the file. There were the pictures I had seen! There was the picture from the picnic—I could hardly believe my eyes. I continued to look through the file. "May I make copies?" I asked.

"You may." answered the librarian.

Dr. George M. Brown
Fanny's Pastor

FRIDAY EVENING, FEBRUARY 12, 1915. TWENTY-TWO PAGES TWO SECTIONS —TWO CENTS

LICE AT WORK PON MURDER OF OUR-OLD INFANT

n Mrs. Morehouse Admits ingling Baby—Housekeeper ew Nothing of It, She Says.

. M. L. AYLES CLAIMS SHE EVER SAW INFANT AT ALL

Morehouse Under Surveil-ice in Hospital—Mentions No Name in Case.

tle light was thrown upon the ised infanticide committed by Roger Morehouse at the home of Mary L. Ayles of No. 153 Hough ie by the testimony of the latter e Coroner John J. Phelan this on. Mrs. Ayles denied all ge of the birth or death of the ve that Mrs. Morehouse told at she had given birth to the and that it was dead.

ording to the story told by Mrs. , the Morehouse woman, who is at the Bridgeport hospital un-urveillance by the police, was not rder at her home. She said that vas simply staying there for a time, despite the fact that be-of the condition of the woman, Ayles had repeatedly asked her ake arrangements to go to a al.

Claim Admission.

. Morehouse is said by the po-o have admitted the details of leged murder, the infant having strangled by use of a garter cord. tive Sergeant Peter Hall, who ed the woman at the house on h avenue last night, found the of the child wrapped in news-s and old clothing, with the about its little throat. The ge was concealed in the attic house, and Mrs. Ayles told the er today that she had never op-it.

geant Hall refused to tell how olice learned of the affair. The is that Lieutenant Hazel re-word over the telephone late ight, and sent Sergeant Hall to igate. He found conditions as , and made the arrest. He sked today in the presence of er Phelan how the matter came nd, but refused to state.

Didn't Tell Police.

geant Hall denied that Mrs. had notified the police. He y stated that the manner in the information was received not to be made known.

Mrs. Ayles told the coroner was about to move to No. avenue, and would probably Monday. She declared that ad long contemplated taking a hed apartment for herself and wo sons, if there was no other n which she could induce Mrs. house to go to the hospital and arrangements for her reception during her anticipated illness in n.

. Ayles stated that she did not boarders and that she had not with her husband for two years. keeps house for her two sons.

NOTED HYMN WRITER DIES TODAY

FANNY CROSBY

PLOT TO DESTROY RAILROAD LINES IS DISCOVERED

Grand Trunk System Sends Warning to Agents—Detectives Immediately Assigned.

PORTLAND, Me., Feb. 12.—The Grand Trunk railway from its headquarters in Montreal has sent an official warning to all its agents in the United States and Canada, of a plot to dynamite property owned by the railroad.

This warning is to the effect that the plot was hatched in California and that the plotters are now speeding across the country towards the east.

Following this notification steps have been taken to guard the railway property here, according to dispatches today.

Detectives on Duty.

Plain clothes men from the Portland police department are on watch day and night over the elevators, freight and passenger yards here.

Detectives in the employ of the Grand Trunk are today speeding west to pick up the trail of the plotters, according to information received from Canada. These detectives hope to pick up the trail and follow the

BANKRUPTCY IS ATTRIBUTED TO BANK FAILURE

Mentes and Pusztai Had Large Part of Money in Burr & Knapp Bank.

Nicholas Mentes and Andras Pusztai, builders and contractors in this city have filed an application in bankruptcy in the United States court and have taken oath that they cannot obtain the money to pay the filing fee. As a firm their liabilities amount to $5,392.21, of which $3143.66 are secured claims. Their assets or paper amount to $3,520 of which $1,320 is amount due them on open accounts and the rest in unliquidated claims. The open account is money deposited in the Burr & Knapp bank.

The Park City Lumber company is the largest creditor, their bill being $2,584.66 on which they hold a mechanic lien. The Frank Miller Lumber company is the largest creditor on the unsecured claims, their amount being $1,390.06. The Park City Lumber company are on this list for $500.

Against Nicholas Mentes, as an individual he is liable for a debt of $300, but he has no assets.

The individual debts of Andras Pusztai amount to $2,632.85, but he

DEATH CLAIMS FANNY CROSBY WORLD-FAMOUS HYMN WRITER

City Loses One of Most Distinguished Residents—Though Nearly 95 Years Old Miss Crosby Was Recognized as Greatest Writer of Hymns in World—Had Composed More Than 8,000 in Addition to Many Cantatas.

HAD BEEN FAILING IN HEALTH FOR PAST YEAR

Stricken Blind When Two Years Old, She Suddenly Developed Ability to Write—Compositions Appear in Hymnals in Every Christian Church in World—"Safe in the Arms of Jesus" Her Favorite Hymn.

Miss Fanny Crosby, the blind hymn writer, and perhaps the most prolific writer of sacred verse in the world, died at 4:30 this morning at the home of Mrs. Henry D. Booth of No. 226 Wells street, where she had made her home for the past dozen years. Miss Crosby's passing away was peaceful and without pain, as if she were falling into a slumber, her everlasting sleep. She had been failing in health for the past year, but there was no apparent illness. It was the weakness of old age, for she was nearing her centennary birthday.

Miss Crosby was nearly 95 years of age, and her death comes as the result of the infirmities of old age.

In the death of Miss Crosby there passes away one of Bridgeport's most distinguished residents for she was not only a national character, but an international one. Her hymns have been translated into every tongue and are recited and sung in every land. She was recognized as the greatest writer of evangelistic hymns in the world.

Blind since a tot of two years Miss Crosby has probably written more songs than any other individual composer in the world. Early in life she developed a tendency for music and when this inclination was encouraged it was found that her compositions were harmonious and clear.

Studied with Famous Masters.

She studied with famous music masters for several years and then decided to make song writing her

Fanny's death notice, Bridgeport, Connecticut newspaper.

Bridgeport Post.

Time to
AUT
BEGINS
See the A
port's

BRIDGEPORT, CONN., MONDAY EVENING, FEBRUARY 15, 1915.

TWENTY-TWO P.
TWO SECTIONS

IN BURGLARY PLAYS POLICE MORALIZATION

ık Business Men—Bad
gement, Jealousy and
e Breaking Involved.

IRDINARY PLANS
PROTECT PROPERTIES

Live in Fear of Raids
urglars—Some Police
helters Disclosed.

burglars can take a safe
front part of a store on
avenue, within two blocks
olice station, throw it down
the rear of a store, blow it
d get away with the loot,
u think it is about time
Vilson got onto his job as
asked one of Bridgeport's
men as he talked over the
of Harry Quinn's saloon.
vening and this morning this
was the talk over the city.
d hear it discussed at social
s, in public places and
usines smen and loud were
inciations of the police.
e inquiry disclosed a most
nary condition of affairs. No
der now thinks his or her
safe, except under ground or
round.
women go out taking all
luables with them. Others
ey and jewels in the rgound.
ake good care not to have
n a few dollars in the home,
vels are kept in the safe de-
lts.
e most astounding moves
necessary are those by Main
rekeepers who are going to
ble every night to move up
fes and cash registers from
to the front of the store, in
that they will be safe from
rs under the glare of electric
m within and without.

Il Enter Front Doors.

that Quinn robbery I don't
at this move will do any
aid one Main street man.
hing we know the burglars
k in the front doors and get
th the goods while the police
n some barn, garage, or home,
pinochle or drinking hot cof-
continued.
ot difficult to find intense in-
n growing all over the city
t of it is directed against the
lepartment. The most seri-

HUNDREDS HONOR FANNY CROSBY'S MEMORY TODAY

First Methodist Church Thronged at Funeral Services of Famous Hymnist.

RELIGIOUS AND PATRIOTIC ORGANIZATIONS ATTEND

Clergymen from Other Cities Pay Tribute—Eulogy by Rev. Geo. M. Brown.

Friends and admirers of Fanny Crosby, the blind hymn writer, from all parts of the state, and from New York, crowded the First Methodist church this afternoon to pay their final devotion to her memory. All the pastors of the Proestant churches in the city were present. A great many clergymen came from out of the city.

D. A. R. Represented.

There were delegations present from the Hartford chapter of the D. A. R. and from the local chapter, who entered in a body. At the conclusion of the services they passed the casket and each member dropped a violet.

Members of the King's Daughters from the various churches of the city were present, the Grand Army of the Republic, the Women's Relief corps of the G. A. R., and other local church organizations.

Largest Funeral in City.

It was the largest funeral service that has ever been held in a Protestant church in this city. Long before the hour of the services the church was crowded, and more appeared to be coming all the time. Allen Sankey, son of the evangelist and president of the Biglow and Main musical publishers of New York, Hubert P. Main, the secretary of the company, Sidney Saunders, and other members of the firm, were present, also Miss Dyer, a noted singer of New York.

The casket containing the remains of the poetess was in front of the pulpit platform and against a great mass of tall palms and flowers that reached nearly to the top of the pulpit. The services were simple, and were conducted by Rev. George M. Brown, the pastor and a personal friend of the deceased, who was assisted by Rev. Henry A. Davenport of the People's Presbyterian church.

To Erect Memorial.

One of the suggestions that came out of the services was that the new Rescue Hall in Bank street be erected to the memory of Fanny Crosby.

Robert Lansing, Counsellor of the State Dept.

ROBERT LANSING, counseller of the State department, is the author of the notes to Germany and England concerning the use of the American flag at sea. The note to Germany, coming as near an ultimatum as could be written without precipitating the country into a war, has been looked on as a model of forceful diplomacy. Taken with the note to England it showed, according to experts in international law, the sympathies of the American government in the great war. Mr. Lansing is about 50 years of age, having been born in Watertown, N. Y. in 1864.

18 MILL RATE IS LIKELY IN FIRST REPORT OF BOARD

May Later Be Pared Considerably—Grand List Totals

RAY AND SHEA NO LONGER TEAM UP IN BILL TELL ACT

Young Mrs. Shea Thought Three Weeks on Road Made Her

GERM NOTE TO I BLOC

Will Not
chantr
Cease
Shipm
for N
tion
Zone
tory N

GREAT I
MERC

Anti-Gern
Kaiser
War
Germa
dent c
ing—I
Taken

WASH
German g
United St
departmer
dor Berns
many is v
announced
merchant
cease its
of food st
combatant
The Ger
war zone
taliatory
sult of
from rule
her purpo
civil popul
Inter
Ambass
livered th
sing said
was of an
and was n

Fanny's funeral article, Bridgeport, Connecticut.

Fanny Crosby

Fanny Crosby

Fanny with Children

Fanny Crosby at age eighty-six.

Fanny Crosby

Fanny in Parlor at 226 Wells Street

Fanny Crosby in parlor of 226 Wells Street

SUNDAY, MARCH 21 IS
NATIONAL

Fanny Crosby Day

Celebrate the birthday of this beloved BLIND SAINT who wrote more than 8,000 hymns. Sing some of her hymns you know so well. Use the Fanny Crosby **Memorial Service,** or the **Pageant,** "The Life of Fanny Crosby."

FREE—Sample copies of THE MEMORIAL SERVICE and THE PAGEANT, and facts about the Fanny Crosby Memorial Home by writing today.

Dr. S. Parkes Cadman

Chairman National Committee

Fanny Crosby Memorial Home for the Aged
150 Fifth Avenue, New York City

Fanny Crosby Day

Beginning of Interest

Every year as we made our way to New England we would visit with our friends, Dave and Debbie Balcom of Cayuga, New York. They enjoyed my curiosity and, after a brief conversation, the questions sooner or later would come around to, "Well what more have you learned about Fanny?"

In the fall of 1995, I decided that there were so many interesting facts about this lady maybe I should become her, in drama, of course. Over the next 6 months I tried to write the drama but there was something missing, something stopping me. How would I pull together all of the different aspects of Fanny's life? This woman was involved in everything! Eventually I gave up.

The following year they asked, "How is the 'Fanny Thing' coming along?"

I explained I put it aside, something was missing. During the discussion it was suggested that I go to Bridgeport, Connecticut to search. Fanny spent the last fifteen years of her life there and it is where she is buried. I thought that it would probably be a waste of time since most of her 'famous years' were spent in New York.

The next morning over breakfast, Dave and Debbie announced that Dennis and I would leave for five days. They purchased tickets on Amtrak and made reservations at a motel. The Balcoms were sending us to Bridgeport and said, "Don't come back until you have what you need to finish the drama!"

This would be an interesting trip for Dennis and me. We had never traveled by train. We had never been to Bridgeport, Connecticut and little did we know this trip would change our lives. We left Utica, New York, and traveled on to New York City, from there to Bridgeport, Connecticut, eight hours in all.

Dennis is the kind of person who likes to have all of his ducks in a row. This was completely out of his realm, to travel without his wheels, to depend on everything falling into place. There were so many things to do—how would we do them without an automobile? How would we get to our hotel? Dennis hates calling a cab.

We arrived in Bridgeport about three o'clock P.M., and our hotel was directly across the street from the railway station. As we checked in I was explaining to the clerk why we were in Bridgeport. I explained that I needed the library...it was three blocks to the left; I needed the Golden Hill Methodist Church...four blocks to the right and the city offices...across the street, one block to the left; the Fanny Crosby Memorial Home, one half mile away and the cemetery a few blocks further. The hotel would gladly take me to either. As we checked into our room, I realized that within 15 minutes of our arrival in Bridgeport, everything was handled.

Later that day we made the first of many trips to the Bridgeport Library. I asked for information and found there was a historical file on Fanny Crosby. Over the next three days I studied and Dennis copied. It was amazing the number of newspaper articles and interviews I found. This was an important lady to the town of Bridgeport. There was even an autographed original of one of Fanny's books. I remembered that she learned to write her name in order to sign her works and legal papers. Much of the information I was lacking was there!

We visited the Golden Hill United Methodist Church, formerly called the Methodist Episcopal Church, this was the church where Fanny was a member. The original building, where her funeral was held, was destroyed by fire and rebuilt just a few years after

Publishers' Advertisement.

Attention is called to the following statement by the Author of this work:

> "'Fanny Crosby's Life-Story" is published and sold for my benefit, and I hope by its means to be a welcome guest in many homes.
>
> *Fanny Crosby.*

It is sincerely hoped by the publishers, that this book may have as large a sale as possible, in order that the story of its loved author may be an inspiration to many people, and that she may be enabled to have a home of her own, in which to pass the remainder of her days.

This book is sent free of postage, for one dollar.

Agents wanted in every church and vicinity, to whom liberal commissions will be paid. In sending for book, state if you wish also terms to agents. Address:

EVERY WHERE PUBLISHING COMPANY,
(Brooklyn Borough)
New York City.

Fanny Crosby's autograph

226 Wells Street the way it would have looked in 1915.

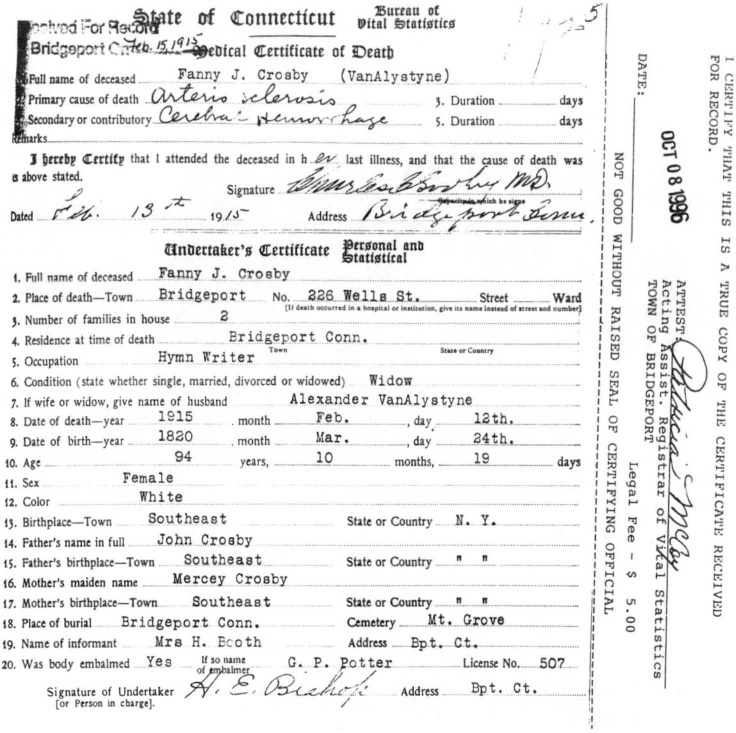

Received For Record Bridgeport Ct. Feb. 15, 1915

State of Connecticut — Bureau of Vital Statistics

Medical Certificate of Death

Full name of deceased: Fanny J. Crosby (VanAlystyne)
Primary cause of death: Arterio sclerosis — 3. Duration ... days
Secondary or contributory: Cerebral Hemorrhage — 5. Duration ... days
Remarks

I hereby Certify that I attended the deceased in her last illness, and that the cause of death was as above stated.

Signature [illegible] M.D.
(Capacity in which he signs)
Dated Feb. 13th 1915 Address Bridgeport Conn.

Undertaker's Certificate — Personal and Statistical

1. Full name of deceased: Fanny J. Crosby
2. Place of death—Town: Bridgeport No. 226 Wells St. Street ... Ward
[If death occurred in a hospital or institution, give its name instead of street and number]
3. Number of families in house: 2
4. Residence at time of death: Bridgeport Conn. (Town) (State or Country)
5. Occupation: Hymn Writer
6. Condition (state whether single, married, divorced or widowed): Widow
7. If wife or widow, give name of husband: Alexander VanAlystyne
8. Date of death—year 1915, month Feb., day 12th.
9. Date of birth—year 1820, month Mar., day 24th.
10. Age 94 years, 10 months, 19 days
11. Sex: Female
12. Color: White
13. Birthplace—Town: Southeast — State or Country: N. Y.
14. Father's name in full: John Crosby
15. Father's birthplace—Town: Southeast — State or Country: " "
16. Mother's maiden name: Mercey Crosby
17. Mother's birthplace—Town: Southeast — State or Country: " "
18. Place of burial: Bridgeport Conn. — Cemetery: Mt. Grove
19. Name of informant: Mrs H. Booth — Address: Bpt. Ct.
20. Was body embalmed: Yes — If so name of embalmer: G. P. Potter — License No. 507

Signature of Undertaker [or Person in charge]: H. E. Bishop — Address: Bpt. Ct.

I CERTIFY THAT THIS IS A TRUE COPY OF THE CERTIFICATE RECEIVED FOR RECORD.

DATE: OCT 08 1996

ATTEST: Patricia McCoy
Acting Assist. Registrar of Vital Statistics
TOWN OF BRIDGEPORT

Legal Fee - $ 5.00

NOT GOOD WITHOUT RAISED SEAL OF CERTIFYING OFFICIAL

Fanny Crosby's death certificate.

I went to the courthouse and received a certified death certificate. Now I knew exactly how Fanny died. In the wee hours of the morning of February 12th, 1915, at home at 226 Wells Street, Fanny Crosby Van Alstyne died from Arterio Sclerosis and a Cerebral Hemorrhage.

Golden Hill United Methodist Church, Bridgeport, Connecticut. Formerly Methodist-Episcopalian, Fanny's home church.

Fanny's death. There are still many historical objects, a cornerstone, and beautiful windows from the original building.

The church historian, Mrs. Lois Weatherby, was extremely helpful and provided me with much of it's history. Both Mrs. Weatherby and I were excited about the drama and we made copies of pictures that each of us collected of Fanny over the years. Before leaving the church, I sang Blessed Assurance in the sanctuary for our own enjoyment. What a lovely sound to hear the words of that great lady come home to her own church; and how wonderfully the churches were built years ago for I needed the help of no sound system.

That afternoon we visited Mountain Grove Cemetery. What a beautiful place! It is a large, old cemetery where many famous people have been laid to rest. To find Fanny's grave one must enter Mountain Grove Cemetery through the main gate on North Street. Go straight until you come to the Elk Monument, turn right. Pass the Elk, turn left and go straight to Section 8. After passing the Section 8 sign go about 100 feet, stop, look to your right and there you will see Fanny's grave along with those of her family. In the family plot you will find the following; see table # 2.

Not far is the large monument to P. T. Barnum. On Fanny's grave there is a small marker that simply says;

Aunt Fanny, She hath done what she could.

Fanny Crosby's original tombstone.

Mountain Grove Cemetery, Bridgeport, Connecticut

Tombstone placed at Fanny's feet by the Bridgeport Historical Society on May 1,1955

On May 1, 1955, the Bridgeport Historical Society erected another stone at her feet. It is a large marble stone about five feet tall by three feet wide and on it is inscribed the following:

In grateful and loving memory of
Fanny J. Crosby
Who inspired and edified
Christians all over the world
by the writing of more than
3000 hymns and poems.
DIED IN BRIDGEPORT, CONN.
FEBRUARY 12, 1915
Blessed Assurance, Jesus is Mine!
Oh what a foretaste of Glory Divine!
Heir of salvation, purchase of God,
Born of the Spirit, washed in His blood
ERECTED BY FRIENDS TO
WHOM HER LIFE WAS AN INSPIRATION

Morris Family Plot, where Fanny Crosby is buried with mother, Carrie and Jule. Mountain Grove Cemetery, Bridgeport, Connecticut.

Fanny Crosby Memorial Home, Bridgeport, Connecticut.

The next day we visited the Fanny Crosby Memorial Home at 1088 Fairfield Avenue. This home was what Fanny wanted so desperately as a lasting memory of her name. It was purchased as a haven for those with nowhere to go and it is still a home for homeless men and women, run by the Bridgeport Rescue Mission. I couldn't help but know that Fanny would be delighted!

The home takes people off the street, homeless, drug-addicts, prostitutes, etc. They may stay for one year if they follow the rules and attend classes. They must be trying to put their lives back together.

I have spent a week in the women's home and heard their "life changing" stories. All of the women were at one time involved in prostitution in order to support their drug and/ or alcohol habit. They now live in a warm home and know the Lord Jesus Christ as their personal Savior.

What a ministry we saw in this place! The Bridgeport Rescue Mission and Mickey Kalman, along with his wife, Beverly, run the home. Mickey was saved at a mission in California.

Mickey Kalman (center) leading praise and worship at the Fanny Crosby Memorial Home.

There was so much in my head, how would I ever be able to sort through it? I went back to the hotel to try and rest but something was nagging at me, go back to the cemetery!

The next day Dennis and I went back to the cemetery. There I spent a quiet time on Fanny's grave. God put within me a strong urge;

Pick up the seed that has been buried here for seventy-six years,
plant it and bring it back to life for My Glory.
Show others what I can do and what I did in and
through the Life and Songs of Fanny Crosby!

It was time to leave Bridgeport, the train was waiting, and all of my notes were neatly put away in my bag. Everything was done. As the train pulled away, I thanked the Lord and asked for His help. "Lord," I said, "you know me, this isn't my field, but I am willing." Thoughts came to my mind faster than I could ever remember, I pulled out my computer and began typing.

Dennis said, "We're back!"

All of a sudden I realized it had been several hours and the drama was completed! That evening I took the time to thank God for making this all possible, for the people of Bridgeport and the Balcoms for their belief in me.

Refining the Drama

Over the next few months I refined the drama. I went the to library to find pictures of costumes, compared them to pictures of Fanny and made the outfit.

Then came the spray for the hair and eyeglasses. Extremely dark bifocal sunglasses were purchased and I was on my way. Keeping my eyes closed during the performance did two things, it helped me concentrate on my lines and helped me to perform as if I were actually blind.

The first performance was nerve wracking. Would I remember all my lines? Would I represent Fanny and the Lord in the best light? Would people even be interested?

They loved it and it has been a great success!

I thank the Lord for allowing me to present this drama around the world and to represent Fanny. What an honor has been bestowed upon me!

Taking Fanny Home to Bridgeport

In 1998 we were back in New England, this time to bring the drama home to raise money for the Memorial Home. We decided to do more investigation for the book. I would like to share my diary of that week with you:

Dear Lord,
Help me to find the things I need to accomplish your will.

Tuesday, September 29,1998

We found Alexander's grave at Mount Olivet Cemetery in Maspeth, New York. The grave was in the Sunny Side section on Border Avenue between Hope Avenue and Clinton Avenue, grave #587, unmarked. The records at the cemetery have Alexander Van Alstiene. I have seen this spelling before and have no idea why there are two spellings. Fanny always used Van Alstyne when she signed her name and on all legal documents. I have never seen her use this other spelling.

We did not find the baby's grave and there are no records at the cemetery of a baby Van Alstyne. I am highly suspicious that she is buried in the same grave as Alexander.

After searching New York City I realized the Institution sat directly catty-corner from what is now Madison Square Garden taking the entire block with lawns running west all the way to the river.

At the turn of the century the Institution was moved. We have visited the school, which is still in use today. We found its halls filled with blind students as well as students with other handicaps. The Institution, founded in 1831 as The New York Institution for the Blind, today is called The New York Institution for Special Education, located at 999 Pelham Parkway, Bronx, New York 10469.

Wednesday, September 30,1998

We have traveled to Brewster, New York to follow the path to Fogginton Road. There we found the home that was built in 1758. In this home, in 1820, Frances Jane Crosby was born. I visited the spot where Fanny sat, and I sat upon the same rock. I could hear the rippling of the water and as I closed my eyes, I, too, heard its music!

Dennis and I then made our way to the Old Southeast Church where Fanny was christened Frances Jane Crosby as an infant.

The church is almost exactly as it was in 1820, there still is no electricity, heat or running water.

We made our way to North Salem. We found the cemetery and foundation for the Old Quaker Meeting House. There Fanny and Mercy lived and worshiped with the Westchester people. The church was built in 1740 and the foundation still exists in the midst of the cemetery.

The sign at Peach Pond has been stolen and more graves have been vandalized. I found acorns all over the ground. As I was picking them up I looked at the huge oak trees, two of them. They were there during Fanny's life. They were a lot smaller, but they were there. I wondered if they knew about the seeds that were planted on this soil other than their own? The seeds that were planted in the heart of a little girl. Seeds that would grow to touch the entire world.

Historical plaque in front of birthplace of Fanny Crosby, Southeast, New York

Fanny's birthplace in 1820 and Fanny's birthplace in 2000.

Rock where Fanny played as it looked in 1820 and 2000.

Yard where Fanny played as it looked in 1820 and 2000.

Old Southeast Church where Fanny was christened as an infant.

Foundation of the old Quaker Meeting place where Fanny and her mother attended 1824-1828. To find the cemetery leave Ridgefield on Rt. #116. Turn right on Rt. #212 (Peach Pond Road). Continue straight until you come to the Old Quaker Meeting House 1740 and Peach Pond Cemetery on the east side of the road.

Hawley House, Ridgefield, Connecticut.

Thursday, October 1,1998

We have traveled to Ridgefield this morning. The home at 212 Main Street was the Hawley's house where Fanny and Mercy lived.

The owner was at home. She graciously invited us in and showed us around. It is a large, lovely home.

The home is once again surrounded by flower gardens. When the new owner was putting in her flowers she found evidence that there had once been gardens on the property. They would have been the rose gardens where Fanny picked the white rose.

Fanny's bedroom would have been on the second floor, facing the east, where the big tree is right outside. She spent many nights praying for schooling by that window.

> Elijah (1783-1869) and Betsy (Smith) Hawley (1780-1875) are buried in the Hurlbert section of the Ridgefield Cemetery. We were not able to find their graves because of vandalism that had taken place in the cemetery.

Friday, October 2,1998

Dennis and I paid a visit to the 226 Wells Street home. The outside of the home has been aluminum sided. We felt that the inside of the home is probably much the same as when Fanny died.

The home is now a duplex, up and down. The present owners invited us in to look around. In the front of the house is a small parlor with a Bay Window connected to a good sized kitchen. On the back of the kitchen is a bedroom and to the side of the kitchen was a bedroom.

On Sunday, October 4,1998,

I presented "Aunt Fanny" to the people of Bridgeport. She has come home after 78 years of silence.

This week has been a lot of work, driving, and frustration trying to find places; but once again, Lord, you have blessed us. We have some great pictures, great video and copies of some really good old photos. Our commitment to you has been greatly strengthened.

It has been fun sharing all of this with you.

Once again I have found that the longer I serve You the sweeter You grow!

With Love & Thanks,
Your Servant,
Darlene

Amusing Events

Humor seemed to surround the life of Fanny Crosby and bringing her back has evoked the same. We have had some comical times during the years of presenting Aunt Fanny.

There was the time in Utica, New York, in a large church downtown, a beautiful venerable gothic Presbyterian Church built at the turn of the century.

Next door to the church was a nineteenth century mansion built by a wealthy family. The house was given to the church years ago. Supposedly their daughter committed suicide in the home and they could no longer live there. It was rumored for years that the mansion was haunted by the young lady's ghost. Someone had even taken a picture of the ghost on the landing of the beautiful winding staircase above the front entrance door.

I arrived a short while before time to start and was promptly sent to the mansion so that no one would see me in costume. With my inquisitiveness I began to look around. As I made my way up the winding staircase I heard the sound of someone coming up the hallway at the bottom. I stopped on the landing, turned around to look down behind me when I saw one of the church Sextons. He caught a glimpse of me on the landing and proceeded to let out a dreadful sound and retreated hastily.

I did not know the entire story or that I was standing in the exact place as in the picture until after the drama that evening. I apologized over and over for scaring the man half to death.

Another time I was in a church in Connecticut. I made an appearance as Fanny in the morning service and trying to stay in character, of course, acted blind. That evening, when the drama was completed, people were coming to the altar and I decided to excuse myself quietly from the stage. As I started down the steps a lady lunged out of the pews to keep me from falling. She, of course was terribly embarrassed when she realized that I was not blind!

One evening we were in Memphis, Tennessee. I finished the drama and retreated to the back of the church where I was grabbed by an elderly lady who proceeded to tell me of singing my songs all of her life. She was so thrilled to finally meet me. That was when I began to realize the power involved in drama. This woman was talking to Fanny Crosby, she honestly felt as though she met Fanny. I had done my job! What a responsibility I felt, also what an honor to represent this powerful lady! From that time I have never taken the job of becoming "Aunt Fanny" lightly. I realized that I must always do my best to represent her and the Lord!

The Video

In September of 1998, we were scheduled for a television interview with Dr. Jimmy Thompson in Norcross, Georgia. I would be interviewed as Darlene for 30 minutes and then become 'Fanny' while he interviewed someone else. When I came on as Fanny, I had a list of questions for Dr. Thompson to ask. After the first question he became so drawn into talking with Fanny Crosby he was mesmerized.

When the show was finished we sat on the set and talked for nearly an hour. Dr. Thompson so loves Fanny's songs and the story of her life that we decided to make a video of the drama. *THE LIFE & SONGS OF FANNY CROSBY.*

Old Friends

"A shade of saddeness steals over me and I ask,
"Where are the friends of my youth,
Oh, where are those treasured ones gone?"...Fanny Crosby

When Fanny would think of the Blind School, instantly the names, Cynthia Bullock, Catherine Kennedy, Mary Mattox, Anna Smith, Imogene Hart and Alice Holmes, her dear friends, would come to mind.

Fanny's lifetime friend, Sylvester Main, died in 1873.

Phoebe Knapp died while in Poland Springs, Maine on July 10,1908 of a stroke.

On December 23,1915 Mr. William Howard Doane died of pneumonia at 84 years of age.

December 26, 1915 Ira D. Sankey died of a heart attack.

William J. Kirkpatrick died of a heart attack while writing a hymn.

Hubert P. Main died October, 1925, at the age of eighty-six.

His firm of Bigelow and Main merged with Hope Publishing Company of Chicago.

George Stebbin went on to set at least one more of Fanny's poems to music before he died in Catskill, New York in 1945, four months short of being 100 years of age.

Fanny's sister, Jule, died of cancer in January 1921 at 80 years of age. She was Fanny's last close blood relation.

Fanny's step-niece, Florance Booth, died in 1935. Florance is buried at Mountain Grove Cemetery, Bridgeport, CT, section #2.

Henry Booth, Florance's husband, died in 1946. Henry is buried at Mountain Grove Cemetery, Bridgeport, CT, section #2.

Eva Cleaveland, Fanny's faithful secretary, died in Bridgeport, Connecticut in 1956.

On May 1,1955 a monument was placed at the feet of Fanny's grave by the Bridgeport Historical Society.

Some Unique Poems by Fanny

When Fanny was 94 years old she wrote the following poem that tells of her conversion experience.

The Valley of Silence

I walk down the Valley of Silence,
Down the dim, voiceless valley alone,
And I hear not the fall of a footstep
Around me, save God's and my own;
And the hush of my heart is as holy
As hours when angels have flown.

Long ago I was weary of voices
Whose music my heart could not win,
Long ago I was weary of noises
That fretted my soul with their din;
Long ago I was weary with places,
When I met but the human and sin.

I walked through the world with the worldly,
I craved what the world never gave,
And I said, "In the world, each ideal
That shines like a star on life's wave
Is tossed on the shores of the Real,
And sleeps like a dream in its grave."

And still did I pine for the Perfect,
Yet still found the false with the true,
And sought, 'mid the human, for heaven,
But caught a mere glimpse of the blue,
And I wept where the clouds of the mortal
Veiled even that glimpse from my view.

And I toiled on, heart-tired of human,
And I moaned, mid the masses of men,
Until I knelt long at an altar
And I heard a voice call me—since then
I have walked down the Valley of Silence
That is far beyond mortal ken.

Do you ask what I found in this Valley?
'Tis my trusting place with the Divine,
For I fell at the feet of the Holy,
And above me a voice said, "Be Mine."
And there rose from the depth of my spirit,
The echo, "My heart shall be Thine."

A Tribute to Cincinnati

What forget thee, Cincinnati,
Lovely city of the West?
Never till the pulse of feeling
Throbs its last within my breast.

I have spent such days of pleasure,
O, such months of joy in thee,
That the very thought of leaving
Brought unwelcome tears to me.

I can see thy stately buildings;
They are all before me yet;
I can see thy fountain goddess
Throw aloft a spray of jet;

Taste, magnificence and splendor
In that work of art are shown,
Far exceeding in impression
Anything I e're have known.

Churches, Sunday-schools and missions
Do thee credit, every one;
For the humble and the lowly
Thou a noble work hast done.

In a church I heard one Sabbath—
And it seemed to me sublime—
Fifteen hundred children singing
"Precious Name" in perfect time.

Thou canst boast a hall of learning
Filled with books of endless store;
And that Wesleyan College numbers
Half a century and more.

What a glorious scene to view it
Grouped with girls of talents rare,
Poring o'er its ponderous volumes—
Not a moment wasted there!

And, among thy sweet environs,
Pleasant thoughts are clinging still
Round the names of dear Mount Auburn,
Clifton Park, and Corryville.
There's a dwelling on Mount Auburn
That my heart remembers well;
I ascend to its veranda,
And my hand is on the bell.
Just the same as when I left it,
Comes the old familiar sound;
Now the door flies quickly open,
And I enter with a bound.
I must calm this burst of transport,
I must stay its sudden flight,
For my brain is growing giddy
'Mid a whirl of gay delight.
With the first warm greeting over,
Up the easy stairs I glide;
By a cheerful grate they place me,
All my wrappings thrown aside.
Then begins a conversation,
And the time flies quick and fast;
By and by a summons calls us
To the closing day's repast.
This is not a dreary picture
Drawn from fancies floating free;
That Mount Auburn home is real,
True to life as truth can be.
What? forget thee, Cincinnati,
Lovely city of the West?
Never till the pulse of feeling
Throbs its last within my breast.

To The Citizens of Bridgeport

Friends, around your growing city,
Rich in beauty, wealth and art,
Cling the best and purest feelings
Ever wakened in my heart.
Dear to me each laughing brooklet,
Dear to me each mossy rill,
And the home of my adoption,
May I call it, if I will?
Home is where our memory lingers,
And our thoughts a vigil keep
O'er the graves our tears have hallowed,
Tears that only love can weep.
Rural cot and stately villa
Nestle 'mid your groves so fair;
And in summer, O how sweetly
Comes the cool and fragrant air!
Once at close of day I wandered,
Musing on your wave-girt shore,
Through your seaside park so lovely,
Where the crested billows roar;
And I thought the birds sang sweeter
Then they ever sang before.
Then I saw in queenly beauty,
Radiance flashing from her eye,
Freedom's goddess bending graceful
From her chariots in the sky;
And she said in solemn accents,
While she held our banner bright,
Crimson with the blood of martyrs,
Gleaming in the rosy light:
From this patriotic city,
When the battle cry was heard,
And the fire of indignation
Every loyal bosom stirred—
From this patriotic city,
Rank by rank and corps by corps,
Rushed they on with lion courage;
Some alas! returned no more.
But their names are not forgotten;

On this monument they stand,
Wreathed in amaranthine laurels
Twined by love's immortal hand.
Then she smiling laved her pinions
In the white foam's dashing spray,
Blessed the monument she guarded,
Spread her wings and soared away.
Then the burst of choral music,
Whence I knew not, filled the air;
Were those patriot souls departed
Hovering in the sunset there?
In that crimson, cloudless sunset
That before me shone so bright,
Did they vanish when its glory
Passed forever from my sight?

Friends, your city, from my girlhood,
Was a treasured spot to me;
Many a summer's glad vacation
'Mid its wilds 'twas mine to see.
Time has added to its beauty,
Changed the haunts I still recall,
But a light from past enjoyment
Is reflected over all.
I can see the picnic gathered
On the beach at evening time;
I can see the full moon rising
In her majesty sublime;
And the fairy boat so graceful
As it glided from the shore,
Till we scarcely heard the echo
Of its lightly dipping oar.
Ah, perchance those simple costumes
Are not held so dear as then,
But have dwindled into shadows
Of the things that once have been.
They were pleasant in their nature,
They were social of their kind,
And they left a healthful pleasure
In the young and eager mind.
Oft I clasp the hand of many
That in early days I met

When I hither came to visit
Mother, sisters, spared me yet;
But some tender links have parted
From the chain affection wove,
And their hallowed dust is sleeping
In your lovely Mountain Grove.
And my full heart bending o'er them
Weeps not hopeless where they lie,
But believing through the Saviour
I shall meet them by and by—
Meet them in the soul's hereafter,
Meet them on the balmy shore,
In the sunny land of roses,
In the Christian's evermore.
Once I stood beside their gravestones,
When the leaves around me fell,
And the branches swayed above me,
And their moan was like a knell;
For a funeral train passed near me
To a grave but newly made,
And an infant in it's beauty
Like a lily there was laid.
What a calm steals o'er my spirit
While in pensive thought I rove
Through the shady walks that circle
Round your quiet Mountain Grove.
It was well and wisely chosen;
And, when future years have fled,
Let no changes that may follow
E'er disturb the silent dead.

O'er your city may the blessing
Of the holy One descend;
May its onward march continue,
And its commerce wide extend;
And among its sweet environs
May the yearly fruits abound;
With the smiles of peace and plenty
May the farmer's toil be crowned.

For Connecticut's State Song

We Suggest the Fanny Crosby Song

Bpt Life. Feb. 12, 1927

Connecticut's State Song.

NO MORE appropriate song could be chosen for the honor of State position along side of laurel, the State flower, than Fanny Crosby's "The State We Honor," which was written in 1908 by the poet laureate of the Daughters of the American Revolution and sung to the tune of "The Red, White and Blue." This song was copyrighted at that time and has been sung many times at patriotic meetings ever since. The song is as follows:

FANNY CROSBY

THE STATE WE HONOR

By Permission of Bigelow and Main Co. N. Y.
Copyright 1908

All hail to the state we honor
And claim, as the place of our birth
The glory and pride of our nation
The spot that is brightest on earth
Unstained by the sword of the tyrant,
The home of he loyal and brave.

Chorus

The home of the loyal and brave
The home of the loyal and brave
Our Connecticut State heaven bless it,
The home of the loyal and brave.

A song for the state that we honor
A song for the wide spreading tree
That grew by our own native river
Nor dreamed what its future might be
But in years when a haughty oppressor
Demanded the charter he gave;
That charter concealed in the darkness
Was hid in the oak by the brave.

Chorus

A voice from the state that we honor
An echo from valley and plain
It bids us remember the watchword
That he who transplants will sustain
'Twas God of the faithful transplanted
Our sires from oppression's dark ways,
He sustained and He is now sustaining
Our home of the loyal and brave.

Chorus

Then hurrah for the state that we honor
Hurrah for our dear native land;
Of America's grand revolution
The daughters united we stand
Not a link from our bond shall be severed
While freedom her standard shall wave
Our Connecicut State heaven bless it
Three Cheers for the loyal and brave.

—FANNY CROSBY.

The Connecticut State Song

In December of 1971, there was a contest given by Governor Meskill to replace the Connecticut State song. Some of Fanny's fans submitted a song she had written in 1908 entitled; *The State We Honor.* It was not chosen but it seems to me, not being from Connecticut, that it would have been a better choice than Yankee Doodle to replace the Yale tune *Boola Boola.*

The State We Honor

All hail to the State that we honor
And claim as the place of our birth
The glory and pride of our nation
The spot that is brightest on earth.

Unstained by the sword of the tyrant,
It's colors triumphanly wave:
Our Connecticut State, heaven bless It,
The home of the loyal and brave.

A song for the State that we honor
A song for the wide spreading tree,
That grew by our own native river
Nor dreamed what Its future might be.

But In years when a haughty oppressor,
Demanded the CHARTER he gave:
That CHARTER concealed in the darkness
Was hid In the OAK by the brave.

A voice from the State that we honor
An echo from valley and plain:
It bids us remember the watchword
That he who transplants will sustain.

'Twas the God of the faithful transplanted
Our sires from oppressions dark wave,
He sustained and He now is sustaining
Our home of the loyal and brave.

Then hurrah for the State that we honor
Hurrah for our dear native land:
Of America's grand revolution
The daughters united we stand

Not a link from our bond shall be severed
While freedom her standard shall wave
Our Connecticut State heaven bless It
Three cheers for the loyal and brave.

Interesting Facts

Mr. William Howard Doane's home still exists in Cincinnati, Ohio. The room added onto the left side was Mr. Doane's music room. In this room he and Fanny spent many hours together writing hymns. It was told to me that this room housed Mr. Doane's water powered organ, one of only two known in the world. The organ was removed when the house was remodeled. I have not been able to find out what happened to it.

William Howard Doane is buried in Cincinnati, Ohio at the Spring Grove Cemetery. To find the grave enter through the main gate on Spring Grove Avenue. Go straight under the bridge. Continue another 600 feet. Stop, look to your left. There you will see a large statue of a Lady holding a Laurel Wreath. This is the Doane family plot and William Howard Doane's grave is to the left of the statue.

Home of William Howard Doane, Cincinnati, Ohio.

Grave of William Howard Doane, Spring Grave Cemetery Cincinnati, Ohio.

The old piano that Fanny once played still exists in an upstairs room of the Water Street Mission. Could it be possible to say that the prints (fingerprints) of Fanny Crosby still exist in the world today?

In 1999 while in Nashville, Tennessee teaching at Ben Speer's Stamps Baxter School of Music, Dennis and I visited the Methodist Museum, The Upper Room. There in the museum were Fanny's doilies.

The museum gave me permission to photograph them for use in this book. These doilies are on display for all to see at the Upper Room Museum, Nashville, Tennessee. Please visit the museum while in Nashville. It is very interesting.

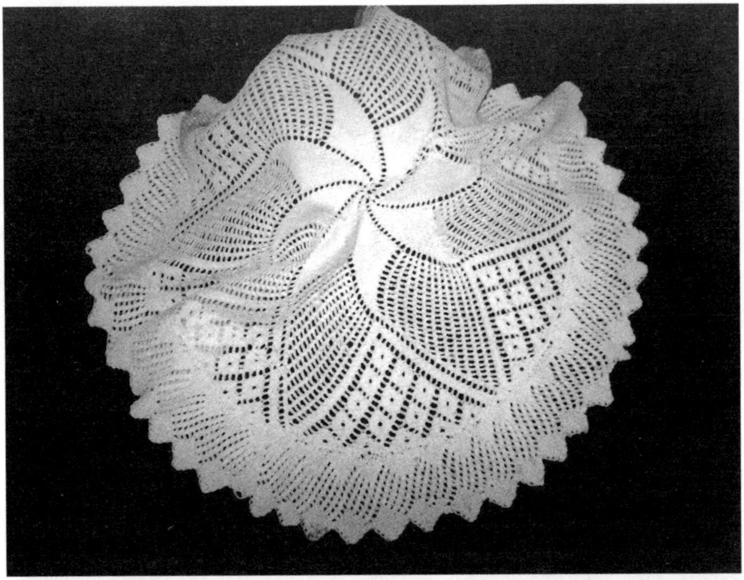

Doilie made by Fanny Crosby.
Used by permission of Upper Room Museum, Nashville, Tennessee.

In 1891, Albert Cusick (Sa-g-na-qua-ten or "He Who Makes Everybody Mad"), an Onondaga-Tuscarora who had been a chief in the traditional government, was ordained deacon of the Wesleyan Methodist Mission. Cusick contributed to the compilation of the Seth Newhouse version of the Constitution of the Six Nations for publication. He was Fanny's Chief when she was made an honorary member. Fanny would take the train to Tully, then to the Onondaga Reservation.

Tully Train Station, Tully, New York, where Fanny traveled to.

The summer of 2000 Dennis and I traveled to the shores of Lake Tully in NY. Three miles from the town of Tully we found the area in which the Onondaga Indians held their annual Round Table.

We searched the area for the Longhouse or area where the Round Table would have been held. Knowing of course that it had been almost 100 years and there would be nothing left, still we looked. We were about to give up when we spotted a road that headed back into a wooded area with a sign that read "Private Property." Of course we went on down the road and as we made a circle I spotted in the woods what looked like a Longhouse. Dennis stopped and I headed out of the car towards the building. Two teenage girls explained to me, as I was peeking in the windows, that their family owned the property and lived in the house next door. I told them I felt it was a Longhouse similar to the one I had been looking for. We went inside and I spotted an old poster-type picture on the back wall. It was a collage of many pictures of the Onondaga Round Tables, this was the actual place I was looking for!!! What are the odds? God is so good!

The Onondaga Reservation is located on Route #11, about eight miles south of Syracuse, New York. There is not much on the reservation other than homes, a school, Indian Affairs Office, three churches and small gift shop.

The Onondaga Indians are part of the Iroquois Nation whose six tribes consist of the Mohawk, the Seneca, the Oneida, the Cayuga, the Tuscarora and the Onondaga.

After coming down from Canada they settled in New York State. The Onondaga tribe settled in the area around Onondaga Lake near what today is called Syracuse.

There are eight clans of the Onondaga Nation. They are the Beaver, Turtle, Bear, Snipe, Wolf, Eel, Heron and Deer Clans. Fanny was an honorary member of the Eel Clan.

The Wesleyan Methodists built their present church in 1895. The Episcopal Church established a small mission in 1816 that flourished. The Methodist Church was established as a mission in 1829 and built the present church in 1848. I paid a visit to the three churches on the Reservation. They look exactly the same today as the pictures of Fanny's time.

The chiefs and council members often took part in church social activities and occasionally attended services. Although not all were converted to Christianity they coexisted peacefully.

Wesleyan Church

Methodist Church

Episcopal Church

Not So Interesting Facts

I have been fortunate enough to have traveled around the world and I must confess that I agree with Fanny on every aspect about America. We have something special here but if we are not careful we are going to lose it. As we travel around our country, Dennis and I are amazed at the lack of respect given to America, our great country. We have even seen Pastors in their own churches not give honor to their flag! When I was a child we were taught that when the flag went by, when reciting the Pledge of Allegiance or when the Star Spangled Banner was played we stood at attention, hand over heart, in respect. Does someone want to tell me when that stopped? Our children are not being taught this respect? Next time attention should be paid to the flag look around. What are people doing? Talking and laughing, and we wonder what is happening to America?

Parents, teach your children to respect the flag of the greatest country in the world!

Grandparents, teach your grandchildren!

Fanny and many of our founders would cry in horror today!

This book would not have been possible to write without a trail of history to follow. A trail of Libraries, Courthouses, Historical Societies, Museums, Biographies, Autobiographies, the Internet and Cemeteries.

From what I have seen happening during my research I fear that 100 years from now this kind of history will not be available. It is amazing the amount of vandalism we encountered in the cemeteries. If I had not been to some of them at an earlier time some of this information would have been lost! When I was a child there was a built in curiosity with the dead but there was also a built in respect. We wandered around the cemeteries but we did not vandalize them.

Metropolitan Duane United Methodist Church
Probably the former Thirteenth Street Methodist Church

False Statements

There seems to be many opinions on the conversion experience of Fanny Crosby. In some books and some internet sites you will find this statement.

> Of Fanny Crosby's conversion experience
> there is nothing written—this seems to have been
> a rather slow and growing grace that Fanny found.
> An unfounded and, no doubt, quite false
> rumor has it that her greater work began after a
> sudden conversion. However concerning this
> mysterious enlightenment of soul she herself gives no
> intimation in her autobiographies.

I beg to differ with that. Fanny's experience in her own words were shared in a previous chapter. Her experience comes directly out of her own autobiography, Memories of Eighty Years, published in 1906.

Her conversion experience took place on November 20,1850 at the Thirteenth Street Methodist Church. After much research I believe that it is now the Metropolitan Duane United Methodist Church.

Will You Meet Us in Heaven?

It would be a great tragedy and I would be forever indebted to Fanny if I did not take this opportunity to ask you if you will meet us in heaven? Fanny and me ? You can! It is only a prayer away.

> Jesus, I need you. I need you as the Lord of my life. I thank you for dying on the cross for my sins. I open my heart and life and receive you as my Lord and Savior. Take control of my life. Thank you for forgiving my sins and granting me eternal life. Make me the kind of person you want me to be. Direct my life to your service and to help others.
>
> In Jesus Name I Pray... Amen

It is important for all Christians to have fellowship with other Christians. Please seek out a local church where you can worship.

Fanny Crosby Lineage

Of Fanny's father, John Crosby, there is little record. He died when Fanny was 10 months of age. Her mother, Mercy Crosby, came from hardy, earnest and devout people. Many lived well into their nineties. Mercy's maiden name was also Crosby and Fanny's lines trace back to Simon and Ann Crosby who settled in Boston, across the Charles River three miles from town, in 1635. Simon was one of the founders of Harvard College and his son, Thomas Crosby, graduated from Harvard in 1653.

Fanny's great-great-grandfather was Isaac Crosby, who was the father of Eleazer Crosby and Patience Freeman, the great-granddaughter of William Brewster. William Brewster was the Elder (Pastor) on the Mayflower.

Through Zachariah Paddack, on her mother's side she was descended from Thomas Pearce and Major John Freeman. Fanny said, "When General Warren was killed at Bunker Hill it was a Crosby, I am told, who caught up the flag as it fell."

Enoch Crosby, the spy of the Revolutionary War, was a cousin of Fanny's grandfather and was written about in the novel by J. Fenimore Cooper, "The Spy."

Simon would be Fanny's four times great-grandfather and Thomas, Fanny's three times great-grandfather. William Brewster would be Fanny's great-great-great-great-grandfather.

She was proud to be related to them and spoke often about them. See table #1

Table #1

Information as complete as I could make it.

1 ***William Brewster,** 1567—1644, Born: Doncaster, Yorkshire, England, Died: Plymouth, Massachusetts. William was the Elder (Pastor) on the Mayflower and also the Elder at the first Thanksgiving service. He arrived on the Mayflower in 1620 and helped establish Plymouth Plantation.
  * Wife **Mary,** 1568-1627, Died: Plymouth, Massachusetts

2 ***Patience Brewster** 1600, Born: Doncaster, Yorkshire, England/**Thomas Prence** 1600

3 ***Rebecca Prence** 1627, Born: Plymouth, Massachusetts
  * Husband, **Edmund Freeman**

4 ***Patience Freeman** 1647, Born: Sandwich, Massachusetts.
  * Husband, **Eleazer Crosby**

**All above information from book: Mayflower Families in Progress, William Brewster of the Mayflower and His Descendants. Second Edition, Published by the General Society of Mayflower Descendants 1997*

1 **John Crosby**, 1440-1502, Born/Died: Holme On, Spaulding

2 **Miles Crosby**, 1483, Born: Holme On, Spaulding Moor, York, England

3 **Thomas Crosby**, 1501-1558, Born/Died: Holme On, Spaulding Moor, York, England
Wife/**Jannett Crosby**, 1506/1569, Born/Died: Holme On, Spaulding Moor, York, England

4 **Anthony Crosby**, 1545-1599, Born/Died: Holme On, Spaulding Moor, York, England
Wife/**Alison Blanchard**, 1550, Born: Holme On, Spaulding Moor, York, England. Died: Wheldrake, Yorkshire County, England

5 **Thomas Crosby**, 1575-1661, Born/Died: Holme On, Spaulding Moor, York, England
Wife/**Jane Sotheron**, 1581-1662, Born: Holme On, Spaulding Moor, York, England. Died: Rowley, Essex, Massachusetts.

6 **Simon Crosby**, 1608-1639, Born: Holme On, Spaulding Moor, Yorkshire, England, Died: Cambridge, Middlesex, Massachusetts. Simon was one of the founders of Harvard College,
Wife/**Ann Bingham**, 1606-1675

7 **Thomas Crosby,** 1635-1702, Born: Holme On, Spaulding Moor, York, England, Died: Boston, Solfolk, Massachusetts. He graduated from Harvard College and though never ordained, conducted services as a religious teacher in Cape Cod, Massachusetts.

8 **Eleazer Crosby**, not much known about Eleazer.
Wife, **Patience (Freeman) Crosby**, 1647, Born: Sandwich, England, great-granddaughter of Wm. Brewster, lived to be 103 and in her eighties made horse-back trips alone to visit friend in Cape Cod, Massachusetts .

9 **Isaac Crosby**, 1719-1819, Born: Harwich, near Cape Cod, Massachusetts. Died: Southeast, New York, fought in the Revolutionary War while in his fifties

Wife, **Mercy Foster**, bore him 19 children.

The youngest of them being:

10 **Sylvanus Crosby**, 1777, born during the Revolutionary War

Wife, **Eunice Paddock**, had six children, Mercy, (Fanny's mother) 1799, Theda 1805, Joseph 1811, Mary (Polly) 1817, one of Fanny's closest childhood friend since they were only 3 years apart in age.

11 **Mercy Crosby**, 1799, Born/Died: Southeast, New York.

Husband, **John Crosby**, Born/Died: Southeast, New York, not much is known about John. It is guessed that he was much older than Mercy, probably closer to Sylvanus' age. In November 1820, after farming in a down pour John came in chilled. The next day he was seriously ill and died a few days later.

2nd Husband, **Thomas Morris**

12 **Frances Jane Crosby,** 1820-1915, Born: Southeast, NY, Died: Bridgeport, Connecticut.

Husband, **Alexander Van Alstyne,** 1831-1902 Died. Maspeth, New York

13 **One Child,** 1859-1859 Born/Died: Maspeth, New York

Table #2

Some of the pseudonyms frequently used by Fanny:

Name or Sign	*Year Used* (May have used on other dates)
##	1873/1886
###	1893
# *"	1891
'*'	1886
***	1881
A.	1882
A. N. O.	
Anon.	1880
Anonymous	1880
V.A.	1872
Viola V.A.	1873
A.Z.G.	1880
Cora Adrienne	1886
D.D.A.	1873
Fannie Jane Alstyne	1869
F. C. Alexander	1869
Lilla M. Alexander	1899

F.J.A.	1877
F.J.V.A.	1877
L.L.A.	1873
Mrs. F.V. Alstyne	1882
A.E. Andrews	1886
Mrs. A.K. Andrews	1884/1889
Mrs. E.L. Andrews	1885
Mrs. K.C. Andrews	1886
Miss Florence C. Amstrong	1890
Floy S. Armstrong	1912
James Apple	1880
Rose Atherton	1882
Alice Armstrong	1893
Mrs. E.A. Barnes	1886
Edna Bark	1884
Carrie Bell	1886
Flora L. Best	1899
Catharine Bethume	1898
James M. Black	1869
James L. Black	1877
Henrietta E. Blair	1890
E.W. Blandly	1890
W.E. Blandly	1879
Florance Booth	1902
Mrs. H.E. Brown	1869
Charles Bruce	1890
Robert Bruce	1887
Hattie Buell	1892
Charles Burns	1890
John Burton	1911
C.	1873
F.C.	1873
F.J.C.	1869
Mary J. Cappe	1889
Leah Carleton	1880/1882
Mary Carlston	1890
Mrs. Leah Carleton	1882
Phoebe Cary	1889

May L. Clayton	1886
Mrs. M.A. Chance	1889
Mrs. Ellen Chase	1884
Children's Friend"	1871
Fannie Church	1892
C.L. Clifford	1890
Mrs. C.L. Clifford	1888
May Clifton	1880
Jessie Clyde	1880
Mrs. S. A. Collns	1903
Eleanor Craddock	1890
Fannie Crosby	1880
Fanny Crosby	1869
Fanny J. Crosby	1915
F. Crosby	1869
F.J. Crosby	1869
Lyman G. Culyer	1899
Lyman J. Cuyler	1898
D.D.	1873
D.D.R.	1872
W.H.D.	1873
Ella Dale	1873
Mrs. Ella Dale	1880
Mrs. E. Dale	1880
Matilda C. Day	1869
Flora Dayton	1889
Mrs. Ellen Douglass	1869
Cora Drienne	1890
Ryan A. Dykes	1889
Rian A. Dykes	1900
Ryan J. Dykes	1889
L. H. Edmunds	1900
Lizzie Edmonds	1892
Lidie Edmunds	1890
Lizzie Edwards	1888
Mrs. Geo. D. Elderkin	1872
James Eliot	1890
Miss Grace Elliot	1884

Mary J. Elliot	1887
James Elliot	1880
F.	1873
F.A.N.	1880
F.A.S.	1892
F.C.	1873
F.C.D.	1878
F.J.C.	1895
F.J.V.A.	1868
F.W. Faber	1880
Fannie	1869
Fanny	1869
J.V.A.	1896
Mrs. Edna Forest	1882
Fanny Forrest	1890
Mrs. Edna Frances	1879
Carrie Frances	1882
Grace J. Frances	1880
Lillian G. Frances	1878
S. Trevor Frances	1879
Victoria Frances	1889
Grace J. Francis	1899
Grace Freeman	1886
Frances Grace	1884
Jennie Garnett	1884
Jenny Garnet	1869
Mrs. Ellen Gates	1869
Ellen M. H. Gates	1875
Jenie Glenn	1890
Jenny Glenn	1872
G.W.W.	1870
Frank Gould	1869
Roland Gray	1898
Dora Greenwell	1890
Mrs. Kate Grinley	1885
Wm. Hammond	1886
Ruth Harmon	1884
J. Hart	1901

Joseph Hart	1886
Carrie Hawthone	1880
Frances Hope	1869
Frances Hops	1872
"W. Hurn	1890
J. Hutton	1893
J.	1869
J.F.O.	1890
J.W.W.	1872
Annie James	1898
Annis L. James	1895
Mary James	1870
Mary D. James	1869
Sarah James	1887
K.D. Jones	1886
Walter S. Jones	1890
Myra Judson	1884
Jennie Johnson	1892
Emma Johnston	1869
Miss. Emma M. Johnston	1899
J.C.K.	1873
Martha Lankton	1887
H.N. Lincoln	1895
Cora Linden	1886
Mrs. Cora Linen	1886
L. F. Lindsey	1880
Grace Lindsey	1893
W. L.F. Lindsay	1882
W. Robert Lindsey	1890
Mable Long	1893
E. Louisa	1876
Minnie B. Lowry	1886
Jeremia Luke	1896
Mrs. Jeremia Thompson Luke	1902
M.A.K.	1890
Kate Marion	1893
Maud Marion	1883/1884
S. Martin	1886

Sallie Martin	1890
Sam Martin	1892
Bertha Mason	1889
Mrs. Rose Matthews	1882
Rose Matthews	1876
Kate Marvin	1892
May Maurick	1897
W. Meade	1896
Albert Midlane	1881
Laura Miller	1886
Abbie Mills	1872
Harriet M'Keever	1896
A. Monteith	1887
Alice Monteith	1887
F.A.N.	1873
Martha C. Oliver	1893
Phoebe Palmer	1876
Edna L. Park	1872
Mrs. M.L. Park	1889
S. D. Phelps	1899
Sylvanus Phelps	1890
Emma Pitt,	1892
Mrs. N.D. Plume	1869
Emily S. Prentiss	1893
Mrs. L.C. Prentice	1889
Jennis Ree	1901
George Sampson	1896
Frances A. Simkins	1869
Mrs. Kate Smiling	1882
Mrs. Albert Smith	1883
James G. Smith	1896
James R. Smith	1869
Sallie A. Smith	1892
Sallie E. Smith	1869
S. M. Smith	1892
Sallie Smith	1872
Sally Smith	1872
Sam Smith	1886

J. L. Sterling	1887
Julia Sterling	1890
Rian J. Sterling	1887
Ryan Sterling	1892
Victoria Sterling	1869
Victoria Stewart	1892
E. H. Stokes	1897
Elwood Stokes	1882
F.A. Stowell	1893
Victoria Stuart	1887
P.K.T.	1893
Nellie Talbot	1900
Ida Scott Taylor	1892
Mrs. R.N. Turner	1890
The Children's Friend	1872
Mrs. Louisa W. Tilden	1876/1896
Mrs. M. L. Tilden	1898
Mary Tilden	1902
Hope Tryaway	1896
V.	1872
V.A.	1882
Viola	1869
Miss Viola V.A.	1872
Jenny V.	1869
Mary V.	1869
Mrs. V.	1869
Mrs. V.A.	1871/1872
Mrs. Van A.	1872
Jenny VanAlstyne	1872
Fannie VanAlstyne	1892
F.J. VanAlstyne	1880
Fannie Jane VanAlstyne	1880
Fanny J. VanAlstyne	1872
Frances J. VanAlstyne	1890
Mrs., Van Alstyne	1878
Mrs. A. VanAlstyne	1882
Mrs. Alexander VanAlstyne	1882
Mrs. F. VanAlstyne	1880

Mrs. Fanny VanAlstyne	1885
Mrs. Fanny J. VanAlstyne	1872
Mrs. F. J. VanAlstyne	1893
Zemira Wallace	1900
Carrie Wilson	1887
Mrs. C. M. Wilson	1867

Some of the 10,000 Hymns written by Fanny Crosby:

A Few More Marching Weary
A Handful of Leaves
A Home Forever There
A Message Sweet is Borne to Me
A Pilgrim's Song
A Shout in the Camp
Abide with Me
Able to Deliver
All For Jesus
All Glory Be Thine
All is Ready
All the Way My Savior Leads Me
All Will be Well
Always Abounding
An Evening Hymn
Anchor Me Home
Angels Above are Singing
Anniverary Song of Praise
Anywhere if Forward

Are You Ready?
Art Thou in Darkness?
Army of Endeavor
As the Bird Flies Home
At the Cross There's Room
Awake! Awake!
Awake! Awake! O Heart of Mine!
Awake! For the Trumpet Is Sounding!
Awake, O Zion's Daughter
Away! Away!
Beautiful Home
Beautiful Sabbath
Beautiful Vale of Rest
Beautiful Waters of Eden
Behold Me Standing at the Door
Behold the Wondrous Love
Believe On the Lord
Bless the Lord, My Soul
Bless This Hour of Prayer
Blessed Are They That Believe
Blessed Assurance
Blessed Bible
Blessed Cross of Jesus
Blessed Feast, The
Blessed Homeland
Blessed Redeemer
Blessed Sabbath Day
Blest, Blest Forever
Blind Bartimaeus
Break Forth, O Joyful Heart
By and By
By Grace are Ye Saved
By the Grace of God We'll Meet
By Thy Spirit Lead Me
Calling for You
Casting Your Care Upon Him
Children Sing
Choose Ye Today

Christ Is Risen!
Christ the Lord Is King
Christian Brother, o'er the Main
Church Rallying Song
Close My Heart No More
Close to Thee
Come Boldly to the Throne of Grace
Come, Come Away
Come, for All Things are Ready
Come, Great Deliverer, Come!
Come, Oh Come, with Thy Broken Heart!
Come to the Fountain!
Come unto Me, Ye Weary
Come with Joyful Anthems
Come with Rejoicing
Come, ya Sinners
Coming Today!
Conquering Now and Still to Conquer
Consecration
Dark Is the Night
Dear Jesus, Canst Thou Help Me?
Dismiss Us With Thy Blessing, Lord
Draw Me Nearer
Draw Me to Thee
Every Day and Hour
Faith in Jesus
Faithful Unto Thee
Far as the East from the West
Father in Heaven
Father, Lead Thy Little Children
Fill Me Now
Forward! Hear the King's Command
Fountain of Mercy
Gather Them In
Gathering Out of Tears
Gathering 'Round the Banner
Gentle Shepherd, Save Me Now
Give Me Jesus

Glad Tidings
Gladly We Will Go
Glory Ever Be to Jesus
Glory to God, Hallelujah
Go and Tell Jesus
Go on Your Way Rejoicing
Go to Thy Savior
Go Work in the Vineyard
God Leadeth
God So Loved the World
God's Holy Church Shall Triumph
Good-night Till We Meet in the Morning
Great is the Lord
Great Jehovah, Mighty Lord
Hand in Hand
Happy Day of Joy Returning
Happy in the Saviour's Love
Happy Resting
Hark! There Comes a Whisper
Haste to the Field of Labor
Hear and Live
He Came to Save Me
He Comes
He Feedeth His Flock
He Hideth My Soul
He Is All in All to Me
He Is Coming
He Will Hide Me
Healing at the Fountain
Hear and Answer Prayer
Hear Our Prayer
Hear Us, O Savior!
Heavenly Father, We Beseech Thee
Here from the World We Turn
Hide Me
Hide Thou Me
His Child Forever
Hold Thou My Hand

Holy Bible, Book Divine
Holy, Holy, Holy Is the Lord
Holy Is the Lord
Home at Last
Home of the Soul
How Oft in Holy Converse
How Precious the Promise
How Sweet the Hour
I Am So Glad That Jesus Came
I Am Thine, O Lord
I Came to the Fountain
I Cannot Let Him Go
I Have Entered Beulah Land
I Know 'Tis the Voice
I Must Have the Savior with Me
I Will Cling to the Cross
I Will Go
I Will Not Be Long!
I Will Praise Him
I Will Praise the Lord To-day
If I Come to Jesus
I'll Be a Sunbeam
I'll Bear It, Lord, for Thee
I'm A Pilgrim
In the Book of Life
In the Hush of Early Morning
In the Morning
In the Twinkling of an Eye
Is It There?
It is the Lord my Savior
It Reaches Me
It was Spoken for the Master
Jesus Is Calling
Jesus is Passing This Way
Jesus Is Tenderly Calling You Home
Jesus, My All
Jesus, My Only Hope
Jesus, Saviour, on Thy Breast

Jesus Will Give You Rest
Joy and Light
Joyful Praise
Joyfully Sing
Just a Word for Jesus
Keep Me ever Close to Thee
Keep Step
Keep Thou My Way
Keep Thy Faith Steady
King of Kings
Lamp of My Feet
Laurels, Fresh Laurels
Lay It Down
Let Me Lean on Thee
Let the Master In
Let Us Away
Let Us be Sure
Lead Us to Thee
Light of the Wandering
Like a Wayward Child I've Wandered
Like an Army We are Marching
Little Friends of Jesus
Little Temples
Lo, the Day is Over
Lo, the Golden Fields are Smiling
Look Up! Ye Weary Ones
Lord, Abide with Me
Lord, Here I Am
Make Me a Blessing To-day
Making Melody
March, March Away
March Steadily Onward
Marching in the King's Highway
Marching On
Marching with Gladness
Meet Me in the Morning
Meet Me There
Mercy is Boundless and Free

Merry, Merry Chiming Bells
Mighty to Save Us
More Like Jesus Would I Be
More Love to Thee, O Christ
My Hearts Dear Home
My Light and Song
My Savior First of All
My Song Shall Be of Jesus
My Soul Shouts Glory
Nature's Praise
Near the Cross
Nearer Home
Nearer the Cross
Nearer to Thee
Never Give Up
Never Shone a Light So Fair!
No King but Christ
No Sorrow There
O Be Saved
O Beautiful Bethlehem
O Beautiful Land
O Bless the Lord
O Bless the Saviour's Name
O Blessed Bible
O Brother, Life's Journey Beginning!
O Child of God
O Church of God, Arise!
O Come, Weary One
O Eden, Dear Eden
O Fly to Him
O My Savior, Hear Me
O Prasie His Name
O Receive Him
O World of Joy Untold
Oh, Come where Love is Bending
Oh, How Sweet When We Mingle
Oh, Precious Words!
Oh, 'tis Glory in My Soul

Oh, to Be Nearer
Oh, to be over Yonder
Oh, What Are You Going to Do?
Oh, Wonderful Word!
On Let Us Go
On the Banks Beyond the River
On the Great Highway
One more Day
One Sweetly Solemn Thought
Only a Beam of Sunshine
Only a Little Way
Only a Step
Only Believe
Only Thy Garment's Hem
Onward, Ye Pilgrims
Open the Gates of the Temple
Opening Hymn
Our Day so Dear
Our Fatherland
Our Festive Song
Out in the Sunshine
Out of Bondage
Out on the Desert
Over and Over Again
Over the Ocean Wave
Over the River
Over the Tide
Pass Me Not, O Gentle Savior
Perfect Trust in Thee
Praise and Magnigy our King
Praise Him, Praise Him
Praise the Lord and Worship Him
Praise, Praise His Name
Praise the Rock of Our Salvation
Praise to Thee, Mighty One
Praise Ye the Lord
Precious Golden Grain
Precious Treasure, Thou Art Mine

Press Forward, O Soldier
Press On!
Press Onward
Prodigal Child
Pure Within
Redeemed
Redeemed, Prasie the Lord
Rescue the Perishing
Rest at Home
Rest by and by
Rest over Jordan
Revive Thy Work, O Lord!
Rock in the Desert
Room for the Penitent
Sacred Fountain
Safe in Glory Land
Safe in the Arms of Jesus
Save Me at the Cross
Saved by Grace
Savior, Like a Shepherd Lead Us
Savior, More Than Life
Saviour, Thy Dying Love
Say, Will You Meet Me There?
Scatter the Seeds of Kindness
Send the Gospel Light
Shall I Be Saved Tonight?
Shepherd's Fold on High
Showers of Blessing
Sing unto God
Sing On
Sing with a Tuneful Spirit
So Near to the Kingdom!
Some Sweet Day, By and By
Something for Jesus
Sound the Alarm!
Speak to Them Gently
Speed Away
Speed for Thy Life

Stand by the Right
Steadily Marching On
Stepping in the Light
Sweet Sabbath Eve
Sweet Story of Jesus
Sweetly Resting
Take Care of Me
Take the World, but Give Me Jesus
Tell It Out with Gladness
Tell It to Jesus
Tell Me the Story of Jesus
Ten Thousand Thanks to Jesus
Tenderly He Leads Us
Tenderly Pleading
That Sweet Story of Old
The Blood Washed Throng
The Bright Forever
The Child of a King
The Christian Flag
The Cleansing Fountain
The Cleansing Wave
The Everlasting Hills
The Everlasting Song
The Good Ship Zion
The Guiding Hand
The Greatness of His Mercy
The Hope Set Before You
The King Is Coming
The Lights of Home
The Lion of Judah
The Lord in Zion Reigneth
The Lord is My Refuge
The Man of Galilee
The Master's Call
The Morning Draweth Nigh
The Morning Land
The Morning of Life
The New Song

The Palace of the King
The Pilgrim's Journey
The Prodigal Child
The Rainbow Round the Throne
The Savior Precious
The Saviour with me
The Shadow of the Rock
The Shepherd's Fold on High
The Story Must be Told
The Summer Land
The Water of Life
The Waiting Guest
The Way of the Cross
There Will I Follow Thee
There Is a Green Hill Far Away
There's Power In Jesus' Blood
There's Room for All
They That Be Wise
They'll Soon be O'er
This I Know!
This My Plea
Thou Mighty To Save
Thou My Shield
Thou will Defend us
Though Kindred Ties Around Us
Though Your Sins Be as Scarlet
Through the Valley of the Shadow
Thy Hand Upholdeth Me
Thy Holy Spirit, Lord, Alone
Thy Saviour Knows Them All
'Tis the Blessed Hour of Prayer
To Jesus I Will Go
To the Work
To God Be the Glory
To-day the Saviour Calls
To Victory
Too Late
Tread Softly

Trust in the Promise
Trusting in Thee
Trusting Jesus (2)
Trusting Thy Promise
Under Thy Shadow
Unsearchable Riches
Up and Away
Upward and Onward
Victory through Grace
Watch and Pray!
Wait on the Lord
Waiting for the Promise
Waiting for Thy Coming
Walking in the Good Old Way
Washed White as Snow
We All Can Do Good
We All Can Do Something for Jesus
We Are Coming Home Tonight
We Are Going, We Are Going
We are Passing Away
We are Singing on the Way
We Never Grow Weary of Telling
We Praise Thee, We Bless Thee
We Walk by Faith
We Will Sing the Old, Old Story
Welcome for Me
Welcome to Glory
We'll Give Our Hearts to Jesus
What a Gathering
What a Refuge
When Christ Arose
When Each Other's Face We See
When I Stand on the Streets of Gold
When the Burden Bearer Came
When the Dewy Light Was Fading
Where He Leads Me
Where Is My Sould To-night?
Where Is Thy Refuge?

Where My Saviour Leads
Whom Have I in Heaven?
Whosoever Will May Come
Why Do the Holy Angels Sing?
Why not To-night?
Whom Have I in Heaven?
Will Jesus Find Us Watching?
Will the Angels Come?
Will You Come?
Wonderous Glory
Yes, There Is Pardon for You
Yielded to God
Young Soldiers for Jesus

Bibliography

Quotations from Fanny's Original Book Memories of Eighty Years

Quotation from the: *Bridgeport Post*, February 12,1915 and February 15,1915.

Quotation from the: *Bridgeport Post*, September 29,1972

Quotation from the: *Baptist Life* February 12,1927.

Pictures used by permission of the Upper Room Museum, Nashville, Tennessee.

Pictures used by permission of the Crosby Commons, Shelton,Connecticut.

Illustrations by Wendy Kakos, Wakeman, Ohio

Special Thanks

I would like to take this opportunity to thank all who helped gather data needed for this book.

First, my best friend, the Lord Jesus Christ for giving me the privilege of writing this book.

My husband, Dennis, for driving me everywhere and anywhere I needed to go to do research while I put this all together.

A very special thank you to Dr. Kenneth and Paula Hemphill who encouraged me to write this book.

To special folks, Debbie and Dave Balcom, Jack Clark, Bob Krupp, Ralph McGinnis, Marion Robinson, Dr. James Thompson and Gloria Thompson.

And finally to everyone who reads this book allowing me to share Fanny's story with you, a big thank you! You are all very special to me.

Fanny closed every speech with the Mitzvah Benediction and so we shall again today;

"May the Lord watch between me

and Thee,

While we are absent, one from the other.

To Order More Books

FANNY CROSBY STILL LIVES

Music Videos:

The complete drama LIFE AND SONGS OF FANNY CROSBY

A complete concert SPREAD THE WORD

Cassette Tapes & Compact Disks:

AUNT FANNY SINGS AGAIN
I AM HEALED
MASTER OF THE WIND

Cassette Tapes Only:

AFTER ALL
BROKEN HANDS
SHADOW OF THE STEEPLE
HE'S AT IT AGAIN
CAROUSEL OF OLDIES

To place an order, please contact:

Neptune Ministries, Inc.
P. O. Box 1081, Naples, FL 34106
(941) 455-1254 or (800) 637-2736
dneptune@sprynet.com
www.darleneneptune.com